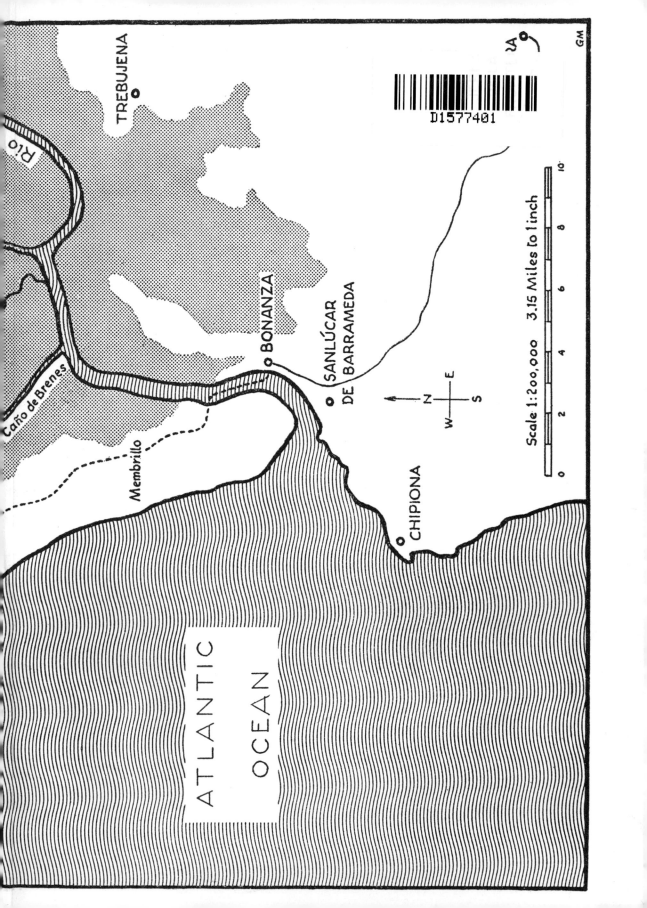

TREBUJENA

Río

Caño de Brenes

Membrillo

BONANZA

SANLÚCAR
DE BARRAMEDA

CHIPIONA

ATLANTIC
OCEAN

N
W — E
S

Scale 1:200,000   3.15 Miles to 1 inch

0   2   4   6   8   10

GM

D1577401

The Trail to the Wilderness

Oh for a lodge in some vast wilderness,
Where rumour of oppression and deceit,
Of unsuccessful or successful war,
Might never reach me more.

Wm. Cowper (1731–1800)

PORTRAIT
OF A WILDERNESS

The story of the
Coto Doñana Expeditions

———

GUY MOUNTFORT

ILLUSTRATED BY ERIC HOSKING

———

Introduction by
FIELD MARSHAL THE VISCOUNT ALANBROOKE
K.G., G.C.B., O.M., G.C.V.O., D.S.O., D.C.L.

HUTCHINSON OF LONDON

HUTCHINSON & CO. (*Publishers*) LTD
178–202 Great Portland Street, London, W.1

London Melbourne Sydney
Auckland Bombay Toronto
Johannesburg New York

★

First published 1958

*Set in thirteen point Bembo type, and printed at
The Anchor Press, Ltd., Tiptree, Essex, on paper
made at South Darenth, Kent, by Horton Kirby, Ltd*

To Don Mauricio González Díez,
without whose generosity and unfailing
enthusiasm the Coto Doñana expeditions
could not have taken place

CONTENTS

ILLUSTRATIONS

* in colour

ILLUSTRATIONS

ILLUSTRATIONS

ILLUSTRATIONS

All photographs are by Eric Hosking, with the
exception of the Frontispiece and Plate II by Roger Peterson,
Plates XX *a* by E. R. Parrinder, Plate LIV *c* by John Raines,
and Plates XVII *a*, XLIII *a*, XLVI *a*, LI *a*
and LIX *b* and *c* by the author.

Line drawings are by Penelope Mountfort and the author

INTRODUCTION

BY FIELD MARSHAL THE VISCOUNT ALANBROOKE

In the preface to this book the author draws our attention to the effect of the relentless process of man's influence on nature, which is taking place at an accelerating and alarming rate, always at the expense of the haunts and homes of the wild-life of this world. He then puts before us the beauties and treasures of the Coto Doñana and impresses on us the importance to mankind of maintaining its preservation. All those who have the pleasure of reading PORTRAIT OF A WILDERNESS must realize the great debt of gratitude owed to him for so ably riveting attention to the international importance of the Coto Doñana as one of the very few great sanctuaries remaining in Europe. How fortunate it is that this wild-life paradise is in the able and sympathetic hands of its present owners, who fully realize its importance!

Through the medium of his pen the author has painted a picture that cannot fail to appeal to all nature lovers and to stir their interest in the preservation of all remaining nature reserves against the advancing flood of ever-expanding civilization.

The treasures contained in such a sanctuary cannot be fully appreciated without a close and scientific examination; Mr. Guy Mountfort is to be congratulated on his appreciation of this fact and on the leading part he took in organizing the three expeditions on which his book is based. In the selection of those to take part he ensured that full attention was given to the scientific side of the nature observations and that these should, whenever possible, be supplemented by both photographic and cine-photographic records. The results achieved have provided a comprehensive contribution to the existing knowledge of the fauna of southern Spain.

To my mind the value of these expeditions was enhanced by the fact that they were private ventures by groups of enthusiasts, bearing no form of sponsorship, but brought together by that freemasonry of ornithologists which knows no barriers of class, profession or nationality. The feelings of comradeship between all members of the expeditions are clearly brought out in the narrative, but in view of the enthralling interest of their studies it would indeed have been strange if those taking part had failed to succumb to the strong binding influence engendered by their work.

The two earlier expeditions were fortunate in having Dr. Roger Peterson among their members; his contributions can well be realized when one bears in mind the great services he has rendered to ornithology in illustrating those invaluable *Field Guides* to the birds of both America and Europe. The frequent references to him by the author bear witness to the important part he played on the Coto Doñana.

The past decades have shown an ever-increasing interest in bird-life in this country. This can in a great part be attributed to photography and the facilities it has provided for the reproduction of pictures of birds in natural surroundings. In this respect Mr. Eric Hosking stands in a category by himself and in recent years he has built up a world reputation as a bird photographer. He was a member of the last two expeditions and on both occasions surpassed himself in the beauty of his work. Many of his pictures of birds and animals were of species being photographed for the first time. Some idea of the value of his work can be formed from the selection of his photographs which illustrate this book.

The cine-photographers of the expeditions obtained colour films of the majority of the birds of interest. These have now been combined into composite films, which have been extensively shown throughout the country and have thus contributed in drawing public attention to the qualities of the Coto Doñana as a nature reserve.

I had the pleasure of taking part in two of the expeditions. In the pursuit of my hobby of bird photography I had previously had opportunities of filming well over one hundred species of birds, but never in my life had fortune placed me in such a cine-photographer's paradise as the Coto Doñana. Constant perfect light for colour photography and countless different species to work on made one wonder whether it might not all be just a happy dream. There was however no rude awakening from this dream, for tangible proof remains in the shape of films which can be turned on at a moment's notice to bring back those wonderful days spent with some of the twenty new species not previously filmed by me.

Throughout the expeditions one factor dominated all others and without this our expeditions would have been doomed to failure and disappointment. I refer to the outstanding generosity of our Spanish hosts. In Don Mauricio González Díez we were very fortunate in having with us a keen and experienced local ornithologist, who entered thoroughly into the objects of our researches and took a prominent part in them. But irrespective of the ornithological bonds that exist between him and the other members, he and his father, Don Manuel González Gordon, and all members of his family, displayed a hospitality and kindness of such unique quality as to contribute in a great measure to the success of the expeditions and certainly to the happiness of the members.

I cannot close this Introduction without a final word of tribute to the leader of the expeditions and the author of this book—Mr. Guy Mountfort. His ability, technical knowledge, enthusiasm and charm were an inspiration to all of us. Something of his high qualities may be gathered from the pages of his book and the felicitous style with which he has portrayed events of the expeditions and the birds, beasts and reptiles of the Coto Doñana. His vivid descriptions of the wild-life, combined with the excellent word pictures of the country it inhabits, cannot fail to bring back the happiest of memories to all who were fortunate enough to accompany him.

Alanbrooke
F. M.

AUTHOR'S PREFACE

It is a sobering thought that it is now almost impossible to find a spot in the whole of crowded England where one may pass an hour without either seeing or hearing evidence of human enterprise. Ubiquitous aircraft drone across our skies. Electricity pylons, railway lines and roads march across what a brief century ago was virgin country. As the nation's population and its standards of living rise, so the red-brick tentacles of suburbia sprawl ever more widely around our teeming cities. Artificially created lakes, 'introduced' foreign vegetation, the bulldozer and the diesel tractor remould the diminishing landscape year by year. Drainage schemes, agricultural pesticides and industrial pollution upset the ecological balance of almost every form of wild life. Necessary or inevitable as these things may be to the nation's survival in a competitive world, the penalties which follow in their wake cannot be ignored. Our insatiable demand for food, minerals and timber has denuded the land of trees to such an extent that we now have a smaller proportion of woodland than any country in Europe. Nothing remains of our original forests and the list of our lost species of mammals and birds is a sadly long one.

This relentless process of man's influence on nature is taking place at an accelerating rate throughout the world. While feverishly exploiting, despoiling or exterminating the natural resources of the land, we are now polluting the very air we breathe. Not even the remote atolls of the wide Pacific can escape the fall of radio-active dust created by our misadventures in the realm of atomic fission.

A new race of man has arisen, the town-dweller, who can no longer support separation from the mechanized paraphernalia of what today passes for a civilized existence. When he visits the country he deliberately takes with him the shackles binding him to the domestic, business and political preoccupations which have become an integral part of his life.

Lest he sever them he is loth to stray far from a telephone, a radio set and his favourite newspaper. Above all he must not be alone to realize his state of helpless dependence. We all know at least a few such people, men and women who have lost their primitive love of the good earth and all it represents. After generations of town-dwelling, they represent the ultimate product of the industrial revolution. Nevertheless, the British are still predominantly, if sometimes nostalgically, nature lovers. No other nation shows more interest in gardening, nor devotes more time to books and lectures and radio and television programmes concerned with natural history. Neither has any other country so many natural history societies, both popular and scientific. Not unnaturally ornithology is the branch which has the widest appeal; our apparently unquenchable interest in birds has indeed recently been referred to as 'ornithomania'. If it has become a mania it is at least a wholesome one, arising from an innate psychological response to the beauty and freedom of these multi-coloured little creatures, which mysteriously navigate trackless oceans to nest so confidingly among us and delight us with their varied songs. To people with this interest, whether based on sentiment or science, I hope this book may appeal. The story of the Coto Doñana expeditions is a reminder that although we in Britain have lost or destroyed so much of our natural heritage, there are fortunately still a few, a very few, small areas of wilderness remaining in Europe where nature reigns unchallenged in all her splendour.

In our lifetime two world wars and an agonizing civil war have raged around the Coto Doñana, without so much as an echo disturbing its profound peace. The Moorish invasion of the eighth century, which first laid waste and afterwards enriched the whole of Spain, left no trace there but a few crumbling watch-towers, today the established homes of Peregrines and Jackdaws. Even the ancient *Palacio*, dreaming through the centuries and now sheltering behind its whispering screen of great Eucalyptus trees, seems so much part of the natural beauty of the scene that one can scarcely believe it has not always been there. No roads lead to the Coto. To reach its fastness one must still travel, as did the noble

Dukes of Medina Sidonia on their hunting parties in the fifteenth century, by sailing up the broad Rio Guadalquivir from Bonanza and then riding on horseback for five or six hours, through the woods, across the desert and along the boggy edge of the great *marismas*.

In this wild paradise half the bird species of Europe have been seen, some in such numbers as to stagger the most *blasé* ornithologist. Red Deer and Fallow Deer still roam the scrub in their hundreds. Droves of Wild Boar plough the rich earth for roots, and in the springtime the blood-curdling cries of the courting Lynx still chill one's spine during the small hours of the night. Here in this ideal Afro-European climate and vegetation the ferocious Ocellated Lizard, the Mongoose, the Polecat, the Genet, the Wild Cat and numerous snakes compete for domination of the undergrowth, while a dozen species of vultures, eagles and other raptorial birds contend for the mastery of the skies.

The literature of the Coto Doñana is chiefly restricted to the writings of the shot-gun naturalists of the period of 1875 to 1910, Abel Chapman having made by far the most important contribution. Information was also contributed by Lord Lilford, Willoughby Verner, Howard Irby, Howard Saunders and others. The Rev. F. C. R. Jourdain and George Yeates published accounts of short visits made in the nineteen-thirties. The sum of these observations, which, with the exception of Chapman's, were based on only brief encounters with the complex fauna of the Coto, made it clear that a more serious study might produce very valuable results, particularly if it could be carried out on a comparative basis during several seasons. It was fortunate therefore that, in planning our expeditions in 1952, 1956 and 1957, I was able by chance to choose periods representing three dissimilar seasons—an average spring, a late spring following abnormal frosts and a spring of almost unprecedented drought.

Our principal object was to learn the status of the bird populations of the Coto. Secondly to examine their ecological relationships. Thirdly to learn what we could about their migratory movements through the Coto. A number of the rarer species, which had never previously been examined in any detail, were selected for special behaviour studies and

19

photography, for the camera is today an essential tool of science. An impression of the dimensions of the photographic task may be gained from the fact that we exposed some 6,000 negatives and 50,000 ft. of cinema film in colour. Though our work was chiefly ornithological, opportunity was taken, as time permitted, also to study the mammals, reptiles, insects and flora of the region, as all these obviously influenced the lives of our primary subjects.

The story of the expeditions has had to be much condensed in this volume. It is not always presented in strictly chronological order, the combined observations frequently being grouped in the interests of economy of space and to avoid repetition. Those readers who may wish to see more details may do so in the reports which are being published in the journals of the British Ornithologists' Union and of the Sociedad Española de Ornitología.

A total of twenty-one people took part in the three expeditions. Four were French, two American and two Spanish, the remainder being British. Six were members on two occasions, only Don Mauricio González Díez and I participating in all three. Members were selected on the basis of particular qualifications for the work in which they would be involved. Some were world-famous figures; all were well known in ornithological circles. The task of composing a correctly balanced team for an expedition is always a difficult and sometimes an embarrassing one. There is never any shortage of volunteers. Following a broadcast on the second expedition I received several dozen letters from people of all ages, imploring me to let them take part in the next one. A schoolgirl offered to sew and mend for us and a bricklayer who had served with a cavalry regiment in the first World War offered to look after our horses and mules. These urgent pleas and many others like them were hard to deny. But our numbers had to be strictly limited and experience had taught me that personal knowledge of the candidate was essential. Expeditions can be ruined if personalities clash. Our teams were therefore chosen with scrupulous attention to good companionship. Looking back on their work, I can only say that I was very proud to have been chosen to lead them, for three better qualified or more co-operative bands of enthusiasts would have been very hard to find.

I am particularly indebted to Mr. Eric Hosking, who acted as deputy leader on the last two expeditions, not only for the able manner in which he carried out this task, but also for directing all our photographic work. The selection of his own pictures, illustrating this book, is of a quality which speaks for itself. Many of them are unique, of species of birds and beasts never previously photographed. Only the privileged few who have worked with him can know the combination of high technical skill and extraordinary patience which produced such masterpieces. He has the unique distinction of having photographed the majority of the birds on the British list. I was delighted to be able to induce him to make these expeditions abroad and am proud to introduce such superb examples of his new work.

The onerous task of sifting and recording the multiple observations of every expedition member was admirably undertaken by Mr. James Ferguson-Lees, who laboured for a matter of months after the last two expeditions on the preparation of the detailed reports. As one of the editors of the magazine *British Birds* he was admirably qualified for this task. No member was more active in the field, or covered more ground, and none saw so many different species of birds as this tireless young man. I am grateful to him for his kindness in reading the manuscript of this book and for his helpful comments on it.

Our cinematographers deserve special acknowledgment for the many long hours they passed immured in sweltering hides while the rest of us were riding about the Coto. There was always good-natured rivalry between the photographers and the field parties, each declaring that it suffered the greater hardships. Having shared in both activities I count the honours even, but I know that the cinematographers, whose heavy equipment had to be carried chiefly by hand, were often reduced to complete physical exhaustion. Those who shared this important task so successfully were Field Marshal Lord Alanbrooke, Dr. Roger Peterson, Mr. George Shannon, Mr. Jerry Jamieson and Mr. Eric Hosking.

To Lord Alanbrooke I am greatly indebted, not only for enabling the expeditions to procure special equipment through War Office channels, but also for using his personal influence in official circles to facilitate our passage across several frontiers.

I am very grateful to Admiral of the Fleet Lord Mountbatten for waving a magic wand over the seemingly insurmountable problem of the movement of our heavy stores and equipment through Gibraltar. From Rear Admiral R. S. Foster Brown, Flag Officer Gibraltar, we received the utmost assistance and a quite remarkable demonstration of the smooth efficiency of the Silent Service.

My deep gratitude must also be expressed to the Spanish Ambassador of that period, His Excellency the Duke of Primo de Rivera, whose keen personal interest in our work resulted in our being received everywhere by the Spanish authorities with the utmost courtesy and co-operation.

I thank Mr. Max Nicholson for writing a most valuable chapter for this book, summarizing the ecological study of the Coto Doñana which he and Don Antonio Valverde Gomez carried out during the third expedition. In this connection I also thank Mr. John Naylon, who generously permitted us to draw on his specialized knowledge of the geomorphology and hydrography of the Guadalquivir delta, beside which the Coto is situated.

I must thank Sir Gavin de Beer and Dr. W. E. China for the loan of equipment from the British Museum (Natural History), and Mr. S. J. Turpin for assistance in classifying our entomological collection. I thank Dr. G. Taylor and Mr. R. D. Meikle of the Royal Botanic Gardens at Kew for similar services in respect of our botanical collection so painstakingly compiled on the Coto Doñana by Lady Huxley, with the assistance of Sir Julian Huxley and Lady Alanbrooke. My thanks go also to Dr. H. G. Vevers of the Zoological Society of London, for his help in the classification of reptiles and amphibians. To the British Broadcasting Corporation and to Messrs. Kodak Limited I record my thanks for the loan of sound-recording equipment and generosity in connection with our photographic tasks respectively.

Every member of the expeditions is most deeply indebted to the joint owners of the Coto Doñana, the Marqués del Mérito, Don Manuel González Gordon and Don Salvador Noguera. It was an unforgettable experience to be given the freedom of this magnificent property, to be able to make our headquarters at the historic *Palacio* and to enjoy the willing services of the faithful *guardas*, who never failed us in any emergency, no matter how strange some of our requests must have seemed to these delightful people.

My personal gratitude to my very good friends Don Manuel González Gordon and his son Don Mauricio González Díez can never be adequately expressed. Their generous help in the planning and execution of the expeditions was boundless. They did everything in their power to make our visits to Andalucía not only immensely rewarding but in every way enjoyable.

Lastly I express my thanks to all members of the three expeditions, for their skill and devotion to our common task of compiling the material on which this book is based. If it should earn commendation, the credit will be largely theirs.

WOLDINGHAM
SURREY

THE HISTORY OF THE COTO DOÑANA

THE early history of the Coto Doñana is a fascinating one. For nearly five hundred years the region was a hunting reserve of the Dukes of Medina Sidonia, whose ancestral seat at Sanlúcar de Barrameda is close by on the opposite shore of the Rio Guadalquivir. Judging from the earliest engravings portraying hunting scenes on the Coto, it was in those days well forested. There is indeed a popular belief that many of the ships of the Spanish Armada were built of timber from this property. Felling, charcoal burning and the encroachment of wind-driven sand from the Atlantic coast have since combined to denude much of the westward area, though new plantations have recently been added.

I am indebted to the Duchess of Almazán for her kind permission to quote the following facts extracted from the late Duke's admirable *Historia de la Monteria en España*, published in 1934. A document dated 1495, presumed to refer to the Coto, shows that the third Duke of Medina Sidonia required his townsfolk to procure 'as many deer and stags as possible' for re-stocking the forest. The oldest surviving record in which the name of the property is actually quoted, however, was dated 16 July 1599. In this a Captain Antonio de Silva, acting for the Count of Niebla, sold 'all the small game of the forest of Doña Ana' to one Alonso de Ribera. The title 'Conde de Niebla' was always given to the eldest sons of the house of Medina Sidonia. The name 'Doña Ana' referred to the wife of one of the Dukes, though her exact identity is uncertain. We know that the fifth and sixth Dukes, Don Alonso and Don Juan, married in turn Doña Ana of Aragón; the seventh Duke, another Don Alonso, who was the Admiral commanding the ill-fated *Invencible*, also married a Doña Ana, daughter of King Gomez de Silva and the famous Princess of Eboli. In quite recent years the title of the property has been contracted to 'Coto Doñana', meaning the estate or hunting reserve of Doña Ana.

During the past 300 years probably all the Kings of Spain have hunted deer and boar on the Coto Doñana. The visit of Felipe IV in the spring of 1624 is perhaps the most interesting and best documented of the many royal hunting parties arranged by the ducal owners. To mark this occasion the then Duke not only enlarged and entirely refurbished the *Casa del Bosque*, as the present *Palacio* or hunting lodge was then known, but built a great tented encampment capable of housing the multitude of courtiers, huntsmen, guests and servants who accompanied the Sovereign. The labour and expense were enormous and torrential rains greatly hampered the task of transporting the necessary materials and stores the many miles across the wild terrain. At the height of the preparations the elderly Duke was smitten by what was probably a stroke, which deprived him of the use of his left leg. Nevertheless, says the contemporary historian, 'with irons on his leg and spurs on his heart and not heeding his illness, he applied his all to the greater service of his King'. Stables, coach-houses, barns, kitchens, oven, larders, quarters for the servants and beautifully furnished tents hung with costly tapestries were all erected. Among the stores, brought first by river and then by ox-cart and mule, were 8,000 planks, 60,000 nails, trunks of table linen, cutlery, glass, porcelain, lanterns, torches, gunpowder, swords, furniture, damasked table-cloths and many tons of foodstuffs. The cost of transportation alone amounted to more than 12,000 ducats, a fortune in those days. All game killed within twenty leagues was ordered to be sent to the Coto, while it was strictly forbidden to kill or disturb any game on the property itself. After forty-five days and nights of labour, all was finally ready on 13 March. The Duke was now completely bed-ridden at his palace in Sanlúcar. Heartbroken not to be able to greet the King, he sent his son the Count of Niebla, his brother Don Alonso and his cousin the Marqués

26

of Ayamonte, with a cavalcade of buglers and huntsmen in elaborate costumes and trappings, to meet him near El Rocío, on the northern boundary of the Coto.

The glittering royal *entourage* arrived to the clamorous welcome of 12,000 people who had assembled in this remote and wild country. No women were present, for this was a hunting party and the Duke forbade the weaker sex, except for travelling entertainers, to set foot on his estate. Fireworks filled the sky that night and lavish gifts were exchanged. The Duke sent the King, amongst other things, an engraved silver casket containing one hundred pairs of gloves and fifty embroidered fobs; other gifts for the King's party included a red dressing-gown richly embroidered with gold and silver, linen shirts, gold trays and crystal flasks.

Next morning the King asked to see a bullfight. Within an hour and a half a ring was erected and nine splendid Andalusian bulls were then fought and killed. The King was next invited to show his skill as a marksman, which he did by shooting three running bulls from the balcony of the *Casa del Bosque* with his harquebus, a primitive gun mounted on a support. In the afternoon he went riding and in the evening watched a play. The following day he went to see the fishermen casting their nets at La Barrosa and spent the evening duck-shooting from a boat on the Laguna de Santa Olalla, declaring repeatedly that he had never enjoyed himself more. Two days later, after a glorious spell of hunting, the King left the Coto on horseback at 5 a.m. after attending Mass. Arriving at the river bank, he had a banquet with his hosts and set sail down river for Bonanza and Sanlúcar, past rows of ships firing salutes. From Sanlúcar he travelled by royal coach to visit the ailing Duke who, still fretting that he had not paid sufficient tribute to his beloved King, presented him with a priceless rose diamond.

It is almost impossible today, in the utter solitude of the Coto Doñana, to imagine the transformation which the visit of Felipe IV and his retinue must have caused. No trace of the event has survived except the additions made at the time to the *Palacio*.

Throughout the succeeding centuries the Dukes of Medina Sidonia entertained many notabilities on the Coto Doñana, besides the Kings of Spain. Among them is said to have been the painter Goya, who is thought to have painted one or two pictures while staying at the *Palacio*, notably the famous 'Majas'. The Austrian Crown Prince Rudolph, of Mayerling fame, also stayed there, as did the sportive Empress Eugénie, who was accompanied by the Princess Anne Murat.

In 1901 the property passed out of the hands of the house of Medina Sidonia, being sold by the final representative of the family, the then Conde de Niebla, to William Garvey, of Jerez de la Frontera, who is said to have recovered the cost of purchase within two years by the sale of pine timber. He continued to let the hunting to a small society of four members, known as the *Sociedad de Monteros*. It had three English members, Abel Chapman, Alexander Williams and Walter J. Buck, the last-named being the local British Vice-Consul at that time. The fourth member was Don Pedro N. González, Marqués de Torre Soto, the father of one of the present owners. The English members were renowned sportsmen and hispanophiles. The two books *Wild Spain* and *Unexplored Spain*, which Chapman published in collaboration with Buck, in 1893 and 1910 respectively, dealt extensively with the Coto Doñana and its wild-life. I shall refer to them frequently later. The emphasis in these books was focussed primarily on the larger mammals and birds as targets, but for the first time birds too small to be worth powder and shot, as well as the reptiles, insects and plants of the Coto, were studied and described by an expert naturalist. Chapman was the first to draw attention to the importance of the region as a major causeway, through which myriads of migratory birds pass each year between the western coast of Europe and North Africa, and to the Afro-European nature of the local fauna.

In 1910 William Garvey died, leaving the property to his brother Joseph, who died in 1914. The title then passed to a niece married to the Duke of Tarifa, one of the leading sportsmen of Spain. The *Sociedad de Monteros* thus came to an end. The Duke set about improving the hunting by the judicious planting of Stone Pines and other trees and thickets in zig-zag formation, to provide alternate cover and open spaces. He and his friends, including the González family, hunted over the property until 1928, when, after the death of the Duke and Duchess, it went to the Duchess's sister, the Marquesa de Borghetto. The northern two-thirds of it were then purchased by a syndicate composed of three great local landowners, the Marqués del Mérito, Don Manuel M. González and Don Salvador Noguera, in whose enlightened custodianship it now remains. The southern portion belonging to the Marqués de Borghetto remains completely unspoilt and there is not even a fence dividing the two properties. Although still used for the occasional and strictly controlled hunting of Red Deer, Wild Boar and Lynx, the priceless value of the Coto as a wild-life refuge is now fully recognized. Today it is probably the most important and most richly populated sanctuary in Europe.

Unfortunately little is known about the history of the *Palacio* itself, where we made our headquarters for the three expeditions to the Coto Doñana. The age of the original fabric probably dates back to the early part of the sixteenth century, but it was not until 1624 that it was 'renovated' and extended to something approaching its present form. The little balcony from which Felipe IV shot the three bulls may have been specially constructed for his visit; it is reached from the dining-room and overlooks the miniature bull-ring. There is a charming panel of stone sculpture between the top of the balcony door and the deeply tiled roof, depicting a hunting scene. In the dining-room hangs a copy of the famous portrait of Felipe IV by Velasquez, gun in hand and a faithful hound at his side. Like most old Spanish buildings, the *Palacio* is built in a hollow square and presents an uncompromisingly stern face to the outside world. Most of the exterior windows are ten feet from the ground and are heavily barred against intruders. One enters the cobbled courtyard through a yawning archway cut into the massive white-washed outer wall; at night this is closed by heavy iron-bound doors, which are obviously of great age. Above and on either side are three coloured religious tiles or *azulejos*, the one on the right depicting *Nuestra Señora del Rocío* (Our Lady of the Dew), whose history I shall describe in a later chapter. In one corner of the courtyard stands a tiny chapel, exquisitely decorated inside and with a single bronze bell suspended beneath an arched support on the roof. In another corner is a well. The servants' quarters, kitchens and store-rooms occupy the ground floor of the main building, which extends along three sides of the court. The living quarters above are reached by a stone stairway. Echoing corridors lead to the many bedrooms, the doors of which all bear inscriptions of the names and titles of past illustrious guests. The walls of the corridors are lined with faded photographs of hunting parties, proudly standing by the carcases of their victims. Leading off the dining-hall is the 'King's Suite', in which so many monarchs have slept; the last to do so was the late Alfonso XIII, who dearly loved to indulge his superb marksmanship and skill at pig-sticking on the Coto.

The great hall, or main living-room, has a high ceiling of arched timbers and a massive fireplace, in which logs of Juniper or Stone Pine burn merrily and aromatically on a chill evening. Around the walls hang a hundred heads of stags. Even the chandelier suspended in the centre of the room is composed of antlers. Opposite the fire is a rather indifferent copy of Titian's portrait of Carlos I of Spain, with his favourite boar-hound Sampere. The original, now in the Prado, was painted in 1533 and earned the artist the title of Conde del Palacio Lateral. On the wall at the far end of the room is an historically interesting framed map of the Coto, bearing the fading inscription, 'Drawn from observations and cross bearings taken by Abel Chapman and Walter J. Buck, in 1902'; we found this to be accurately drawn and constantly useful. The *Palacio* is in good repair and in recent years has been modernized by the addition of two bathrooms and excellent plumbing, without loss to its almost mediaeval charm. I never succeeded in counting the number of rooms in the building. On special occasions, such as the annual pilgrimage to the shrine of Our Lady of the Dew, as many as one hundred people have slept within its walls.

Behind the *Palacio* are barns, and a hen-coop on stilts (as protection against Foxes), out-houses and the usual domed oven, where the round loaves so typical of Andalucía are baked. Next to the oven is a great mound of pine-cone fragments, the fuel used for baking. In an adjoining barn, where Abel Chapman's famous punt still lies armed with its mammoth punt-gun, one side of the floor is 2 ft. deep in the valuable pine seed extracted from the cones. Some of our members declared the seed to be very tasty; it is a local delicacy. A semi-circle of tall Eucalyptus trees and a few Acacias shelter the *Palacio* on the south and east sides, beyond which to the east stretches the immensity of the *marismas*. To the north is a modern, wind-driven water pump, looking incongruously out of keeping with the scene, and a small cultivated plot, of maize, potatoes and other vegetables, behind thick barriers of Prickly Pear, Bramble and bundles of Tree Heath. Through this a sandy trail winds away among the Cork Oaks towards Martinazo and Algaida. To the west the dark pines of the Pinar de San Agustin can be seen on the horizon, usually with a haze of blue smoke rising from the charcoal burners' symmetrical mounds of sand-encased faggots. To the south a narrow track meanders across the flowering scrub towards El Puntal and the beautiful chain of fresh-water lakes of Sopetón, La Pajas, Santa Olalla, Dulce, El Taraje, El Saillo and El Charco del Toro.

The Coto Doñana proper is today considerably smaller than it was when the Dukes of Medina Sidonia were in power, having been reduced during successive purchases to about 67,000 acres. Fortunately the adjoining properties to the north and south are still largely maintained as hunting reserves, so that the region has lost little, if anything, of its unspoilt solitude. The long sweep of the dazzling white sand beach stretches unblemished for forty kilometres along the south-west border. The eastern side is completely protected by the *marismas*, one of the greatest areas of marsh in Europe. Between these two great bulwarks of the Atlantic coast and the marshes of the mighty Rio Guadalquivir, the Coto has suffered through the ages from two competing invasions—wind-driven sand from the former and the inundation of mud and water from the latter. Only from the northern side of the dry, triangular central region is unauthorized entry likely, but thanks to the vigilance of the fast-riding *guardas* of the Coto the extent of the occasional poaching of deer or heron's eggs by hungry peasants is seldom serious.

A number of quite distinct wild-life habitats are offered by the Coto: the *marismas*, with their vast areas of reeds and mud-flats and low islands of stunted Salicornia (Glasswort); the sand dunes and an adjacent area of desert recalling the Sahara in its fierce desolation; the *pinares* or pine woods; the open scrub, consisting chiefly of yellow-flowering Halimium, Rosemary and Lavender; the wide, open 'rides', cut here and there like fire-breaks through the scrub in order to provide ease of movement and visibility for the stag-hunters; the more bushy areas of Pistachio, Tree Heath, Juniper, Gorse, Broom and Bramble; the patches of open sandy ground, carpeted with miniature plants; the fresh-water lakes, with their verdant, grassy borders and attendant lush vegetation; the thick, aromatic undergrowth among trees and swamps along the edges of the *marismas* and towards the river; and finally the park-like scattered groups of ancient Cork Oaks, with their dense foliage and many hollow trunks. In these varied habitats dwells a fantastic variety of birds, mammals, reptiles and insects, some commonplace, others of extreme rarity and interest. It was to learn the status of this complex fauna, which has changed considerably since Abel Chapman's day, that the three Coto Doñana expeditions were organized.

Red Deer stag of the Coto

1 *a*. The *Palacio de Doñana*, where the three expeditions made their headquarters. *b*. Loading the mules outside the entrance to the *Palacio*

11   *a*. Members of the first expedition examining egg-shells on a peasant's midden.   *Left to right:* François Bourlière, the author, Camille Ferry, Robert Etchécopar, François Hüe.
b. Looking for Great Bustards in the rain-swept corn-fields near Jerez de la Frontera

2

THE FIRST EXPEDITION

EVER since first reading Abel Chapman's *Wild Spain* in the early nineteen-thirties, I had longed to see for myself the fantastic wealth of birds and other animals which he described so vividly. However, I was living in France at that time and could not quite bring myself to believe that Spain could offer greater ornithological riches than France's Camargue sanctuary at the mouth of the Rhône, which had become my Mecca, or that, after half a century, it could still have remained unspoilt. After the war I spent my holidays bird-watching in other countries. It was not until 1952 that a visit to the south of Spain became a possibility. A small group of French ornithologists was planning an excursion to Andalucía and their leader, Professor François Bourlière, invited Dr. Roger Peterson and me to join them. Roger and I had met at the Hawk Mountain sanctuary in the Kittatinny mountains of Pennsylvania. We had gone into immediate partnership, later to be joined by Philip Hollom, in producing the *Field Guide to the Birds of Europe*, which has since been published in eight different languages. Roger had come to England to paint the illustrations. We needed more information about certain Spanish birds and so accepted with alacrity. While planning our journey we happened to mention it to Captain Collingwood Ingram, who is an authority on the natural history of Spain. 'At all costs you must call on Don Mauricio González Díez,' he said. 'He really knows the local birds and can arrange for you to visit the Coto Doñana. I'll give you a letter of introduction.' It was from this chance conversation that the

C

Coto Doñana expeditions and our friendship with Don Mauricio originated. Although our first visit was to be of short duration, it served admirably as a reconnaissance for the two full-scale expeditions which I was to take to the Coto in 1956 and 1957.

The French party consisted of Professor Bourlière, Dr. Camille Ferry and M. François Hüe, with their respective wives, and M. Robert Etchécopar, Secretary of the Société Ornithologique de France. As on all three expeditions, Don Mauricio was to be a part-time but very essential member. It was an admirably assorted group. All were experienced field ornithologists. François Bourlière has few equals in virtuosity in the natural sciences; he is widely travelled and equally at home in a discussion on the mammals of Indo-China as on the flora of the Mediterranean, or the birds of Central America. His work in the new science of geriatrics is internationally known. He has probably done more than anyone to foster the remarkable renaissance of interest in natural history which has occurred in France since the last war. The presence of two such ebullient spirits as my old friend Etchécopar, a cosmopolitan Parisian of Basque descent, and Hüe, a splendid naturalist overflowing with the gaiety and mordant wit of the Midi, kept us in constant good humour. Ferry, a quiet, good-looking young doctor from Dijon, had already done some excellent ornithological exploration in Corsica and elsewhere.

The Bourlières, Roger and I met in Madrid in the middle of April and set out by car on the 300-mile journey to Sevilla, where we were to pick up the remainder of the party. We drove fast until we reached the Sierra Morena, with its spectacular ravines and jagged skyline. This range is less magnificent than the Sierra Nevada, whose 9,000-ft. snow-capped peaks cradle the Spanish riviera in the extreme south, but its stern ruggedness has a particular charm of its own.

We saw little of particular ornithological interest until we stopped the car at the top of a gloomy gorge known as the Puerto de Despeña-perros, at about 2,000 ft. above sea level. Deep below us a torrent raged over its boulder-strewn bed; on the opposite side the mountain rose almost vertically; to our right above us towered a beetling rock cliff, slightly overhanging the road. Small streams of water cascaded in spray down the mossy, fern-decked rocks and trickled in rivulets across the winding road. The air was cold and damp. A more forbidding scene would be hard to find. We were, in fact, standing at the very spot where, in bygone days, bandits were wont to throw the travellers they robbed into the gorge below. Our spirits quickly rose, however, when we noticed scores of birds wheeling above the precipice. All binoculars were focussed on them. The smaller, flitting forms were Crag Martins, neat in brown and white and looking like rather heavy Sand Martins, but without the latter's dark breast-band and with small white marks on the upper surfaces of their square-tipped tails. Above them wheeled a few much larger Alpine Swifts, their long, rapier wings winnowing rapidly. There were Pallid Swifts, too, easily distinguishable against the dark rocks from common Swifts by their white throats and paler plumage. In the vertical crevices of the cliff we counted twenty-five gourd-shaped nests of Red-rumped Swallows and had good views of the birds as they swooped low along the road. This was a good start to our Spanish ornithology! But more excitement was to come, for presently Roger Peterson spotted a Bonelli's Eagle on its nest near the very top of the cliff; we saw its silky white breast and the characteristic white patch between its wings as it rose to fly. A few minutes later an unusual cry from the gorge enabled us to see our first Azure-winged Magpie, conspicuous in its pale blue and pinkish plumage; it flew into the undergrowth below us, its hoarse, high-pitched 'zhreee' echoing against the rocks.

We took a few photographs of this memorable scene and began the long, gradual descent into the verdant and sunlit plain. As we started we passed a lonely, bare-footed goat-herd with his flock, wandering aimlessly in the middle of the road. While we dropped down through the foothills the bird-life grew more abundant. Handsome Black-eared Wheatears bobbed at us from stones and fences on the barren hillsides, occasionally circling in brief display flight and giving their strange, high-pitched little songs, 'schwer, schwee, schwee-oo', as though conjugating an irregular verb. One pair had a nest with four eggs at the side of the road.

We also saw Black Wheatears, stout, jet-black birds with brilliant white rumps. Farther on, Crested and Calandra Larks rose from the dusty verges. Migrant Pratincoles, looking like enormous Swallows, circled over the fields. Presently a covey of plump birds, showing much white on their wings, rose from an Alfalfa crop and went rocketing away in grouse-like but swerving flight. Although Roger had never set eyes on Little Bustards before, it was he who beat us all by a split second in identifying them.

'It's just a matter of remembering the diagnostic field marks,' he said modestly. He has a memory like the proverbial elephant.

It was at this moment that Roger discovered the loss of his Leica camera. He recalled putting it on the stone wall above the gorge while watching the Bonelli's Eagle. There was nothing for it but to turn back. Needless to say, when we reached the spot the camera—and the goatherd—had gone. Roger was inconsolable. The thought of him without a camera, and the expedition only just begun, was more than I could bear. Knowing the loss this would represent to our work, and judging him a better photographer than myself, I took my own Leica and hung it around his neck. It was a hard wrench, but the results later justified the sacrifice and I still had my faithful old field camera for work from the hide. In parenthesis I might add that when Roger later lost my Leica also, on the Coto, I was really cross! Fortunately we found it again, and nobody can possibly be cross with Roger for long.

On the rocky mountain slopes near Saragossa we had found masses of superb pink Peonies, as big as breakfast cups, growing in profusion in the grassy clearings. The rich red plains south of the Sierra Morena were also blazing with flowers. Every Olive grove was bordered with drifts of scarlet Poppies, mauve Lupins, white Moon Daisies, golden Marigolds, crimson Clovers and purple Mallows. We stopped again and again to admire them and at each halt more new birds were added to our list: Rollers, Hoopoes, Golden Orioles, Bee-eaters, Rufous Warblers and Griffon and Egyptian Vultures, to mention only a few. On the road we found a big Terrapin, 18 in. in length, which had been run over by a car; its hard shell seemed none the worse for wear and we put it in the ditch.

36

III *a.* A male Great Bustard, one of Europe's most splendid but increasingly rare birds, photographed in captivity

b. One of two Great Bustards killed by a car while fighting on a farm road. The primary wing-feathers are only half grown

IV   *a*. Don Mauricio González showing James Ferguson–Lees the map of the Coto Doñana drawn by the famous wildfowler–naturalist Abel Chapman in 1902.   *b*. An early engraving of King Felipe IV of Spain hunting Wild Boar on the Coto in 1624

Here, too, we found our first Ocellated Lizard, a stout, blue-green creature 16 in. long. These interesting beasts grow to more than twice this length. They play havoc with ground-nesting birds and have even been known to drag young Rabbits from their holes. They have an unpleasant bite and, though not strictly poisonous, the saliva around their teeth is often toxic. Later we were to see many of them on the Coto Doñana.

We reached the lovely old city of Córdoba, one of the great cultural centres of the old Islamic world, to find the townsfolk celebrating their local spring *feria*. The main square was closed to wheeled traffic and was carpeted with wild Thyme, Mint and other flowers, the heady scent of which drenched the warm air. Handsome young *caballeros* were parading their well-groomed arab horses, with their brilliantly costumed *señoritas* riding pillion. The scene was one of almost mediaeval beauty in a superb setting. We parked the car and visited the thousand-year-old cathedral, with its strange mixture of ornate Moorish, Byzantine and classical Corinthian architecture. Beneath its 850 columns, plaques lining the walls were variously inscribed in Latin, Spanish and Arabic. Every window-ledge and crevice around the nave was heaped with flowers, fruit and sheaves of early corn. We returned outside to gaze up at the ancient spires. Roger silently gazed upwards with us. Finally he pronounced judgment.

'There are Lesser Kestrels nesting in the tower,' he said.

We all burst into uncontrollable laughter. Roger looked puzzled. François Bourlière put his arm around his shoulders and said, 'Roger, *mon vieux*, nothing will keep you from your birds!' This was literally true, for when, to use Roger's own expression, he is 'birding' he applies his complete attention to the subject, with a concentration which is quite extraordinary. It is the combination of this power of concentration and his retentive memory which has made him pre-eminent in his subject. It was not that, with his deeply artistic perception, he was insensitive to the beauty of the cathedral; he merely had not switched off the highly stimulated train of ornithological thought in his mind.

We continued our southward journey. White Storks were now becoming increasingly common and we observed one soaring flock of nearly a hundred birds; we also began to see their enormous nests, perched on haystacks, church steeples and houses along the road. Every old town seemed to harbour its colony of Lesser Kestrels. In a steeple at Tembleque we found twenty-five pairs apparently happily sharing the accommodation with domestic white doves—surely a curious *ménage*! These beautiful little falcons are, of course, primarily insectivorous and we watched them catching flies in mid-air and pouncing on grasshoppers along the roadside. Their gliding flight is exceedingly buoyant and agile, though not very rapid. As they turn in the air, their pale blue-grey heads and tails and burnished copper bodies are very colourful. They are much more vocal than the larger and more solitary Kestrel, crying frequently '*chet, che-che*' in a weak, hoarse voice.

Near Tembleque we saw and heard some Spanish Ravens. These birds have been given sub-specific status as *Corvus corax tingitanus* and they have quite distinctive call-notes. Instead of the usual deep '*prruk*' of the northern European Raven, their most frequent utterance is a resonant, klaxon-like note, which I jotted down phonetically as '*kow*'.

After a quick lunch at one of the excellent State-operated restaurants which occur every hundred kilometres or so along the Madrid to Cádiz highway, François Bourlière, who was driving, put on speed for the last lap of our journey, running parallel to the Rio Guadalquivir. The country was now lush and vividly green, with an increasing number of marshes, over which hundreds of herons and egrets of various species were flying. The exquisite, snow-white Little Egrets and the stockier Cattle Egrets predominated, though Night Herons and common grey Herons and Purple Herons were also plentiful. The Cattle Egrets were often seen feeding among herds of magnificent fighting-bulls and other cattle. There were many Marsh and Montagu's Harriers quartering the reed-beds with their typically wavering flight. Several species of larks flew by the hundred over the crops—some, such as the Short-toed, being obviously still on migration. At a farm where we halted briefly we saw our first Spotless Starlings, as glossy as bluebottles and with louder and clearer whistles than those of our northern birds.

It was nearly dark by the time we finally reached Sevilla, where we were welcomed by the Hües, the Ferrys and Robert Etchécopar. We were dog tired, but it had been a memorable day.

Next morning, this time in two cars, we set out again. By the afternoon we reached Jerez de la Frontera, one of the early bastions against the Moorish invasion and now the centre of the thriving sherry trade. After two days of strenuous travel we were thankful to unpack our baggage and enjoy baths at the well-equipped and smartly furnished Los Cisnes Hotel. Don Mauricio joined us in the evening in the cool, stone-flagged lounge and we dined in state at the customary Spanish hour of ten o'clock. None of us had met him before and we were quickly captivated by this very tall, handsome young man with unfailing good humour and charming manners. Nothing we could ask was considered too much trouble and he set about planning our ornithological explorations with enthusiasm. We were to learn later that his name was an open sesame throughout Andalucía.

The next few days were devoted to exploring the bird-life around Jerez, Cádiz, Cape Trafalgar, the Rio Guadalete, the Laguna de la Janda and the Laguna del Torero, all of which were rewarding. In the beautiful garden of a *bodega* owned by Mr. Guy Williams we were shown a Great Bustard, which had lived there as a pet for some years. Our dramatic introduction to wild Great Bustards is described in another chapter. In another *bodega*, belonging to the González-Byass Company, Mauricio showed us an even stranger exhibit, a number of mice which had become confirmed dipsomaniacs! These little creatures, whose passionate addiction to sherry caused them to abandon their native caution, regularly reduced themselves to a state of intoxication in full view of visitors. A miniature ladder was placed against a full glass of sherry on the ground and several mice immediately scrambled up it, competing eagerly for first place. Having drunk their fill, they fell off the ladder and retired to their holes with a gait which all too plainly proclaimed their shameful condition.

While in Jerez we were taken to see a specimen of that very rare and usually invisible little bird the Andalusian Hemipode. It was, alas, in a small cage. We never succeeded in observing one in a wild state on any of our expeditions. In appearance it was very like a rather small Quail, but with an orange patch on its breast and black spots on its sides. The captive had pale blue eyes. Although so like the Quail it belongs to a different family, the *Turnicidae*, or Button Quails. A few of these birds still frequent an estate near Jerez. They are shot from time to time in the sandy Palmetto scrub areas and in Sugar Beet and other crops. Both Abel Chapman and Willoughby Verner discovered their nests by pure chance sixty or more years ago, in low, dense vegetation, but we could find nobody who had seen one. Hemipodes are said to be exceptionally difficult to flush. The call-note, which I have heard in Morocco, is usually most frequent at dawn and dusk: it is a deep, muffled '*crooo*', increasing in intensity and resembling the distant lowing of cattle, hence the bird's Spanish name *Torillo*, or Little Bull. An old peasant, who was introduced to us as an authority on the Hemipode, told us seriously, 'It blows itself up like a ball and calls like a bull, but it keeps its mouth shut and the sound comes out of its ears.' The bird in the cage had been trapped in a Quail net. Bird-catching as practised in Andalucía is a fine art and many of the peasants are extremely skilful, not only in the use of traps, nets and bird-lime, but also in employing decoys and other devices for luring birds. Blinded Partridge decoys, hanging in tiny wicker cages in the blazing sunshine outside peasant huts, are an all too familiar sight. Our Hemipode specialist was a past master in the use of the *pito reclamo codorniz*, or Quail-call, and could attract these birds from the long grass to his very feet. The beautifully made little whistle consists of a small piece of perforated reed with a variable plunger, attached to a tiny cylindrical leather 'bellows' 2 in. long. The tip of the leather is tapped across the knuckles to produce an exact imitation of the male's piping call '*quic, quic-ic*', or is drawn open more slowly to copy the female's wheezy '*queep . . . queep*'. I obtained one of these whistles, but although I practised many times I could never match the skill of this old ruffian.

We made a short excursion by boat from Bonanza up the Guadalquivir as far as the *salinas*, the immense conical hills of evaporated salt, which can be seen for many miles around. It was on one of these dazzling white hills that a vagrant Snow Bunting was shot on 13 November 1955. This was an amazing record of a bird being found about 1,000 miles south of its normal range, on the only patch of apparent 'snow' in the region. The skin is now in the Madrid Museum.

The banks of the Guadalquivir were literally carpeted with waders. It was impossible to estimate numbers, flock after flock rising as the boat approached. Many of the northern species such as Grey Plovers, Turnstones, Curlew Sandpipers, Dunlins, Sanderlings and Knots were already in full nuptial plumage, though they still had all of Europe to cross before reaching their usual breeding grounds. Avocets, Black-tailed and Bartailed Godwits and Black-winged Stilts were there in their hundreds, as were Kentish Plovers. Other species noted were Curlews, Whimbrels, Ringed and Little Ringed Plovers, Common, Green and Wood Sandpipers, Ruffs, Lapwings, Redshanks, Greenshanks, and Oystercatchers. Overhead flew a procession of various herons, egrets, kites and eagles, including our first pair of Spanish Imperials.

We landed for a few hours on the Coto, near the mouth of the Caño de Brenes, and found the stunted vegetation swarming with Short-toed and Lesser Short-toed Larks and with several races of Yellow Wagtails— the Spanish *Motacilla flava iberiae*, the Grey-headed *M.f. thunbergi*, the Blue-headed *M.f. flava* and the Yellow *M.f. flavissima*. (On our later expeditions we saw several birds which looked like Ashy-headed Wagtails *M.f. cinereocapilla*, but could not be certain without examining them in the hand; the White Wagtail *M. alba* was also seen.) Never in my travels around Europe have I seen so many different races of one species at the same place, but such an incident is typical of the migratory concentration which takes place in this extraordinary corner of Spain.

Over the distant reed-beds dozens of tiny Fan-tailed Warblers were flying, with their characteristic bouncing motion, calling '*dzeep*' at each rise. They were evidently already breeding, but we failed to find any of their beautifully concealed, purse-shaped nests until the 1957 expedition.

On a sandy patch we saw an elegant, long-legged Tawny Pipit, the only one found that year, though we saw a number on later visits.

Farther up the river, outside a lonely *choza* inhabited by a family of sturgeon fishers, we discovered a midden strewn with hundreds of egg-shells of Coot, Great Crested Grebe, Little Grebe, and Mallard. Robert Etchécopar, as an expert oölogist, was excited by several shells which he suspected were Crested Coot's. The fishermen, after examining one of the plates from the *Field Guide* (which was then in proof form), agreed that these birds, which they called *Focha*, as they did the common Coot, were indeed nesting in the reeds not far away and they offered to take us in their punts to see them. These dangerous little vessels, which are constructed so that they can be poled over mud, reeds or water, did not daunt either Robert or Roger for one moment, and, although they got thoroughly soaked in the process, they made good use of them.

The following day Don Mauricio arranged that Roger and I should set off to spend a week on the Coto Doñana, while our French friends continued their explorations on the east bank of the river. We embarked at Bonanza in high spirits and after sailing for an hour and a half up the sunlit river reached the landing stage just north of Las Marismillas. Here we were welcomed by Antonio Chico, the dignified and courteous leader of the *guardas* of the Coto, who had come to meet us with pack mules and horses. Our baggage was quickly loaded into the great straw panniers, or *cerrones*, with which we were to become so familiar and we set off for the long ride to the *Palacio*, where we were to make our base.

The narrow sandy trail led first through high plantations of Eucalyptus, interspersed with clumps of Pistachio and Genista, where noisy bands of Azure-winged Magpies flew ahead of us. Red and Fallow Deer scampered across the clearings and a pack of Pin-tailed Sandgrouse rocketed away to our right. Presently the aromatic undergrowth became more dense and in the occasional marshy patches we caught sight of our first Wild Boar. Orphean and Melodious Warblers and Nightingales sang magnificently in the thickets. The terrain became gradually more undulating and an hour later we came suddenly upon a stretch of dazzling white sand. The dramatic transformation from shady woods to this scorching desert was startling in its abruptness. Roger rode this way and that, busy with his camera. At one stage his horse bolted, but Roger, with binoculars and camera in one hand, managed to keep his seat, shouting, 'What's the Spanish for "whoa"?' The horses now plodded heavily, over their fetlocks in the loose sand, which rolled away in wave after wave to the horizon, under a deep blue sky. We were only skirting the dune area and after half an hour of this hard going we began to see clumps of dark vegetation ahead. These proved to be the crowns of large Stone Pines, which were being buried by the drifting sand. The edge of the dunes sloped sharply down and petered out among a complex of Stone Pines, Juniper and low scrub. The scrub was chiefly composed of *Halimium halimifolium*, a close relative of the Rock Rose *Heleanthemum*. This is a branch of the great Cistus family, with glaucous foliage and large yellow flowers, which bloom profusely in the morning and wither in the heat of noon. It is the most typical plant of the Coto Doñana.

The trees gradually died out and we rode across a great plain, grey-green with scrub and dotted here and there with isolated Cork Oaks and clumps of Tree Heath. Kites, eagles and vultures cruised overhead and various herons and egrets rose from the boggy hollows. Sardinian and Dartford Warblers chattered as we passed and occasional Great Spotted Cuckoos scolded us from the tops of bushes. The trail then swung north-east and in the distance we could see the shimmering haze over the *marismas*, where countless terns and waders were flying.

Finally, after a ride of nearly six hours, including halts, a gleam of white showed against a clump of dark trees on the horizon and Antonio Chico said '*El Palacio!*' It was a thrilling moment. At last I was looking at the famous building which we had come so far to see. Long, white and remote it lay, in the midst of romantically wild country. Not having ridden a horse for six years, I was deeply thankful. When, later, I dismounted, I was so stiff that I could scarcely walk, to the intense merriment of the *Palacio* servants who were assembled outside the arching gateway to meet our heavily laden troop. After the long ride the roaring fire which had been lit in the great living-room was most welcome, for the evening was now chilly and we were saddle-sore and weary.

Bright and early next morning, accompanied by Antonio Chico, we made our first exciting excursion along the Martinazo trail bordering the *marismas*. Before the day was out we had identified nearly one hundred different species of birds, for a great migratory 'rush' was in progress and the vegetation was teeming with constantly flitting forms. This first day was in the nature of sight-seeing, but the following morning we settled down to more serious work. Our intention was to make a rough survey of the region and we planned to ride each day to a different part of the Coto. We obviously had insufficient time for detailed studies, though we obtained an interesting photographic documentation. One of the first conclusions we reached was that two people could not hope to do justice to so large and complex an area, where at every turn there was something new to see. We therefore concentrated chiefly on the region between the mud-flats east of the Casa del Puntal, which were alive with breeding waders, and the great heronry at Algaida, where thousands of Little Egrets, Cattle Egrets, Night Herons and Squacco Herons were breeding side by side. In addition Roger made an excursion south-westward to the Sopetón and Santa Olalla lakes and I explored westward across the scrub to the Charco del Toro, near the coast. References to our more important observations are included in the following chapters.

It was one of Roger's habits to take a last stroll around the *Palacio*, before turning in at about midnight. Late one night, just before his usual perambulation, we were toasting our toes by the fire in the great hall, when I noticed him cocking his head and listening attentively.

'I keep hearing a strange noise,' he said. 'Let's go and find out what it is—it might be interesting.' And interesting it certainly was. When we emerged into the cool night air we plainly heard a strange, loud, rhythmic knocking, coming from one of the Eucalyptus trees. The knocks were in pairs and sounded exactly as if someone was vigorously rapping a hollow wooden box. Peering up into the star-lit tree, we presently made out a slender form lying along a branch. Shortly afterwards it flew,

44

v The spectacular cliffs at Arcos, where large numbers of Griffon Vultures roost; one is seen flying at centre; above, much nearer the camera, is a Lesser Kestrel

VI   *a*. Six Magpie's eggs and (*below*) the eggs of three different Great Spotted Cuckoos, temporarily removed from the same nest.   *b*. A brood of young Great Spotted Cuckoos from another Magpie's nest, showing the considerable disparity in ages

showing white patches near the tips of its narrow wings. It was our first Red-necked Nightjar, a bird neither of us had observed or heard before. On the second expedition we were to see many more, but it was not until the final expedition that a nest with two eggs was found, by James Ferguson-Lees and John Raines; on that occasion the female was photographed and filmed by Eric Hosking and sound recordings were made of its voice by John Parrinder. These were the first pictures and recordings ever obtained of this species. The Red-necked Nightjar is quite visibly more rufous, particularly around the neck, than our familiar Nightjar and is slightly larger, with bolder white patches on the wings. There was a fairly consistent ecological difference between the two species on the Coto, in that the Red-necked seemed to prefer high, bushy vegetation and rather moist ground on the edges of and in the pine woods, whereas the common Nightjar was seen chiefly among scattered trees on dry, open ground. The former was the more numerous of the two. Our sound recordings, made by placing the microphone almost in the nest and also by hanging it near the usual song perches of the male, produced most interesting information. The 'song' of the male was usually a long series of double knocks, '*cut-ock, cut-ock, cut-ock*', at the rate of 90-100 pairs per minute; but it was shown to vary considerably, sometimes being accelerated almost to a continuous, even note and at other times being slowed to single, widely spaced notes. On the third expedition Philip Hollom timed one male singing at the rate of 201 double notes per minute. Rapid wing-clapping was also recorded while the male was courting; Philip heard one male give twelve very rapid wing-claps in succession while chasing a female. While sitting on eggs the female gave a long series of *single* slow knocks, then accelerated to a rate of 400 per minute.

I cannot conclude this account of our first expedition without mentioning another example of Roger Peterson's powers of concentration on ornithology. He and I were riding side by side on the edge of the *marismas* one day and he was deep in a dissertation on the dimorphism of certain herons. Our horses had been splashing along through shallow water, when we came to a patch of dry sand. Without the least warning Roger's horse suddenly decided to roll in it. As it went down, in a flurry of flying hooves, Roger stepped neatly off sideways, watched it abstractedly, without so much as an exclamation, swung back into the saddle when it righted itself and went right on talking where he had broken off. If I had not remarked on the incident I really do not believe he would have noticed it. While perhaps not an expert horseman, he is always completely relaxed in the saddle and trusts his mount as implicitly as he does his friends.

We returned to England after this first visit to the Coto Doñana with hundreds of photographs, note-books crammed and a burning determination to go back as soon as possible. We had been able to examine only about one quarter of the area, but had learned a great deal about the problems involved in mounting and maintaining an adequately equipped and self-supporting expedition. I now also knew enough about the terrain and its fauna to convince me that on our next visit we must have a large enough number of qualified observers to permit field work and photography to be carried out simultaneously in different parts of the Coto, if the results were to have any real value. Moreover we needed the presence of experts in botany, mammalogy and other subjects, besides ornithology. So far we had only scratched the surface. We should have to dig deeper before we found the real treasures.

The Inebriates

VII   *a*. The beautiful Azure-winged Magpie, here shown feeding its young, had never before been photographed. *b*. The Red-necked Nightjar on its nest; this was another rare species which had not previously been studied

3

THE SECOND EXPEDITION

THE first expedition had been little more than a valuable preliminary reconnaissance of the Coto Doñana. The second, in 1956, was to be a fully fledged affair, with a carefully planned programme of work. The number of people engaged was also large enough to ensure that the area would be adequately studied.

Three members of the original expedition took part: Roger Peterson, Don Mauricio and myself. There were seven new members. These were Field Marshal Lord Alanbrooke, Eric Hosking, James Ferguson-Lees, James Fisher, E. R. (John) Parrinder, Jerry Jamieson and George Shannon. We met as a team for the first time at the beautiful London house of Sir Archibald Jamieson, to draw up final plans and to allot responsibilities. Hosking was to direct photography; Lord Alanbrooke, Peterson, Shannon and Jamieson would be our cinematographers; Hosking, Peterson and I the photographers; Ferguson-Lees and Fisher the recorders, and Parrinder in charge of stores and animal transport. Shannon had an additional responsibility as medical officer. Ferguson-Lees, Fisher and Parrinder were to constitute the exploratory field party, though all of us would obviously contribute to this work. Finally, Don Mauricio was to be in charge of all preparations in Jerez and on the Coto before our arrival.

We decided that the main party should fly to Gibraltar on the night of 27 April, proceeding to the Coto *via* Jerez and Bonanza by bus, boat and horse the same day. This would represent twenty-four hours of continuous travel. Two ladies were to accompany the expedition. Lady Alanbrooke was to fly out with the Field Marshal on 6 May, while the Hon. Mariegold Fitzalan-Howard would drive out with Jerry Jamieson, *via* Paris and Madrid, taking the bulk of our heavy gear in the car with them.

On the night of the departure of the main party we assembled at London Airport under the startled gaze of the air-line officials. To save excess baggage charges we were travelling in full marching order, with binoculars, telescopes, cameras and other equipment draped around our necks. Our ruck-sacks and kit-bags made an impressive collection. Roger Peterson, who always carries a stupendous load of photographic equipment, seemed cheerfully unperturbed to learn that his excess baggage charges amounted to more than the cost of his return fare.

We had an excellent flight in the Viscount air-liner and landed at Gibraltar at three in the morning. Some of us then snatched a few hours' sleep, but the others would not hear of wasting the opportunity to go exploring. When they returned at breakfast time they already had an impressive list of birds identified, including Barbary Partridges, and had seen the famous apes of Gibraltar.

We cleared the British and Spanish customs barriers at La Linea successfully. On the far side were Jerry and Mariegold and a large bus sent by Don Mauricio, bearing a sign reading 'Coto Doñana Expedition'. At noon we reached Jerez, where Don Mauricio greeted us at the *bodega* with the news that all the advance stores and food had already been sent to the *Palacio*. The organization had been flawless. We drank numerous *copitas* with our host and set out for the river, where an excellent picnic lunch was served on board the launch.

As we chugged up-river we noticed that, by comparison with our last visit, the shores were almost bare of birds, apart from a few flocks of Grey Plovers, Dunlins, Curlews, Whimbrels and Avocets. Migration was evidently pinned down somewhere by the stiff north wind. Great white thunderheads were piled up into the blue sky over the distant *sierras* and it looked as if we might run into a storm.

VIII *a*. A Pratincole rises from its eggs, which can be seen just below its tail. *b*. One of the Pratincole's attitudes of aggression is illustrated as the bird threatens a neighbour which is approaching the nest from an adjoining territory

IX   *a*. Some Pratincoles showed originality by laying their eggs on dry cow-pats instead of on the bare ground. *b*. The larval Ant Lion lies in wait hidden at the vortex of its pit and flicks sand over victims which fall in, to prevent their escape

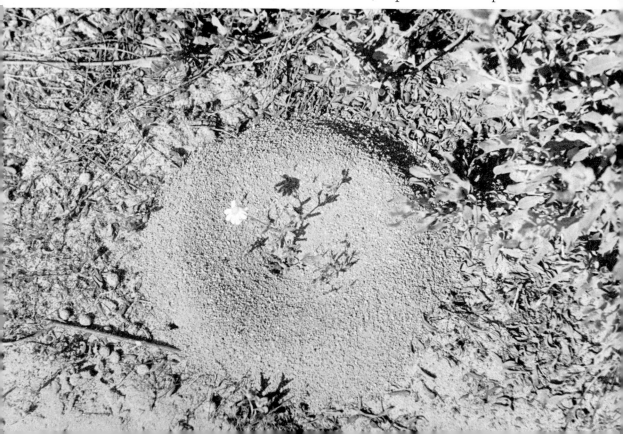

At the landing stage an imposing string of mules and horses stood waiting. Antonio Chico, who was again in charge, was introduced to the new members. More *copitas* were produced and there was considerable gaiety while those who had never previously sat on a horse were hoisted into their saddles. The wise ones, like Roger and myself, who knew the poor calibre of most of the horses, chose mules. On a long cross-country ride the Andalusian mule is not only tireless but much more sure-footed than the under-fed horses; moreover, perched atop the mule panniers, one can ride as one pleases, without stirrups.

The journey to the *Palacio* was a slow one, with halts at hourly intervals to enable aching limbs to be eased. At the beginning of each expedition nearly everyone found riding a hardship, but as time passed and physiques toughened, whole days in the saddle were faced with equanimity.

We had not left the landing stage until four o'clock and I knew that we could not reach our destination before nightfall, but I had not reckoned on the possibility of rain. The first squall fell on us savagely as we were crossing the desert section and within a few minutes we were soaked. Waterproofs were hastily extracted from the mule-packs and we plodded on. The squalls became more frequent and presently a relentless rain began falling. As dusk crept over the plain our gay chatter petered out and the *guardas* had to keep dropping back to whip in the stragglers, for some of the horses were already reduced to a slow walk. It was pitch dark before we reached the Puntal trail and all I could see were the long ears of my mule bobbing in front of me. Many of the horses were stumbling on the sodden, uneven ground, but my mule never varied its steady pace. Ten o'clock was long past when we finally dismounted at the *Palacio*.

Next morning we awoke to glorious sunshine. The Coto had never looked more romantically beautiful. Migration was again in full swing and there was plenty for everyone to see. Almost immediately, a magnificent Spanish Imperial Eagle came gliding low over the *Palacio* to welcome us. Around us the air was full of the twitter of Swallows and

D

49

Goldfinches, while Spotless Starlings whistled like schoolboys as they busied themselves at their many nests under the orange tiles of the roof. A Bonelli's Warbler and a Golden Oriole sang wheezy treble and rich contralto respectively from the Eucalyptus trees. A hidden Bittern was sounding his deep, thumping note at the edge of the adjacent *marismas* and Whiskered Terns circled over the shallows, their hoarse, grating cries mingling with the purring of Bee-eaters. In every direction the bushes were swarming with migrant Woodchat Shrikes. I felt a thrill of mounting excitement as I looked out over the now familiar scene, and listened to the exclamations of the newcomers.

We set off immediately for the Algaida heronry, where hides were to be erected for the photographers and plans considered for the difficult assignment, accepted by James Fisher and James Ferguson-Lees, of making a population census. A small party was dropped off *en route* at Martinazo, to examine a Bee-eater colony, and the field party was asked to start looking for a conveniently sited Kite's nest at which to build a pylon for photography. Soon everyone was hard at work.

Lord and Lady Alanbrooke joined us on the Coto a few days later. I had first seen the Field Marshal in Cairo, at the height of the western desert campaign in 1942. He was known to me then as a great soldier who miraculously had saved the British Army at Dunkirk. It was not until much later that he was to be acclaimed throughout the world as one of the architects of final victory. After the war I added to my admiration of the soldier a new respect for his prowess as an ornithologist and cinematographer. I had therefore been delighted when he agreed to join the second Coto Doñana expedition. With typical modesty he did so on the understanding that he should take his full share of our organized work. His help behind the scenes during the planning stages was invaluable and the films he made during the expedition were of outstanding quality and interest. He and Lady Alanbrooke were very popular, not only with expedition members, but with the *guardas* and staff at the *Palacio*, who would do anything for them. Lady Alanbrooke charmed us all by her unfailing good humour and astonished us by her energy; she and Lord

Alanbrooke were the only two members who completed the strenuous ride to the river in five hours without a halt.

Don Mauricio was unfortunately detained by his business commitments in Jerez, but managed to join us for a few days. His presence had an electrifying effect on the progress of building our pylon, on which we were to mount a hide in order to photograph and film the Kites at their nest in a tall Cork Oak. Vital materials which we needed suddenly materialized and the *guardas* vied with each other to carry out their beloved young master's wishes. It was typical of him that whenever we seemed to be running into any kind of difficulty, on all three expeditions, he appeared at the right moment to solve it for us.

The domestic round at the *Palacio* was organized on very simple lines. We spent as much time as possible in the open and begrudged every moment indoors. Members were detailed in rotation as early morning 'knockers-up' and the one whose duty this was had the only alarm clock. Some members responded to a bang on the door. Others needed sterner measures. James Fisher and Roger Peterson, who shared a room, used to complain bitterly that the 'knockers-up' were altogether too hearty to suit their early morning constitutions. A few early birds such as James Ferguson-Lees and John Parrinder often made a quick reconnaissance around the *Palacio* before breakfast, but most of us were too busy overhauling our equipment for the day's work. Breakfast was a hurried meal, with Jerry Jamieson, our interpreter, holding earnest conferences with the kitchen staff concerning the composition of the lunch packets, according to the numbers of the various working parties. Baggage was then hastily assembled in the courtyard and the arrival of the transport was impatiently awaited. Finally, and nearly always behind schedule, the groups departed.

We seldom returned before dusk. The pretty servant girls of the *Palacio*, Carmelita, Maria, Antonita and Rocío, were usually waiting arm in arm in the archway to greet us as we straggled back, incredibly dusty or muddy according to which part of the Coto we had been working. Equipment was quickly unloaded and there was a concerted rush for *agua fria* to cool our parched throats. Water and bathing facilities were strictly limited and not more than three baths could be obtained on any one evening. Most of us had to make do with a sponge-down at a basin. Ablutions completed, there followed the nightly ritual of writing up the day's records. This was the most difficult task of all to organize. Had it not been for the devotion of the recorders much valuable information would have been lost for ever. It is essential that records should be written the same day. Our procedure was to assemble all members in the living-room, where the recorders went right through the check-list of birds, calling for contributions from all. Every entry was subject to cross-examination, not only by the recorders but by all present. And woe betide anyone who was not sure of his facts! The wisdom of working in groups of two or more in the field was amply demonstrated. Sight records of rarities by unaccompanied observers had scant chance of acceptance unless supported by an unimpeachable wealth of detail.

The allotment of tasks for the following day was worked out during dinner, which was usually at ten o'clock. It was by no means a simple matter. Plans depended on a constantly varying availability of horses and mules, occasionally supplemented by a tractor, and on the movement of a number of different hides, from nest to nest. There were inevitably con-flicting opinions among the members as to which task should take precedence, though the decisions of '*der Führer*', as James Fisher ir-reverently called me, were always cheerfully accepted. Sometimes there were not enough hides to go round among the photographers, though we had brought ten. If it came to someone being odd man out, or doing an unrewarding job, I always knew that Jerry Jamieson would be the first to volunteer. He was the most unselfish man among us and was corres-pondingly popular. The day's plans then had to be explained to Antonio Chico, who somehow always succeeded in providing whatever we needed.

Antonio Chico was liked by everyone. He had spent most of his life on the Coto and was implicitly trusted by the owners. Of medium height and lithe as a leopard in his tight-fitting short jacket and sun-bleached

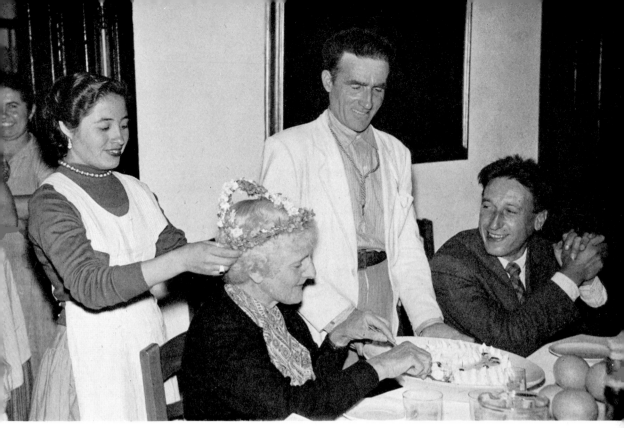

x   *a*. Lady Alanbrooke being crowned with flowers while cutting the cake on the occasion of her birthday at the *Palacio*; on the right is Tono Valverde.   *b*. Sir Julian Huxley (*left*) and Max Nicholson discussing plans for the day's work

XI   *a*. Kentish Plovers nested in large numbers on the dry mud-flats bordering the *marismas*.
b. A pair of Short-toed Larks at their nest; the characteristic dark patches at the base of the neck are well shown in this picture

trousers, he rode his fine arab as though born in the saddle. Beneath his flat-brimmed *sombrero*, his dark, deeply lined face wore an expression of unvarying and completely natural dignity. He seldom smiled, never raised his voice, never hurried, but one had the impression that nothing occurred on the Coto which escaped his notice. His word was law with the *guardas*, yet one never caught him shirking his share of the work. What he secretly thought of our unusual requests I do not know, but he listened to all of them with grave attention and never let us down. Among themselves the other *guardas* often laughed hilariously at the extraordinary exertions to which *los locos ingleses* put themselves, merely to *look* at birds! I remember some of them being convulsed when they saw us searching for and dissecting the regurgitated pellets of fur and bones beneath an eagle's nest, an occupation which they obviously regarded as the ultimate evidence of lunacy. In only one minor respect did Antonio Chico fail us and this we soon realized was inevitable. Like most Spaniards he had an inherent contempt for the passage of time. At the beginning of each expedition it took me a few days to break the enslavement to clocks which is part of modern life. I was therefore at first irritated when our picnic meals, promised by mule-pack at noon, arrived without apology at three-thirty. But I soon found myself content to wait; as Howard Irby pointed out in 1875, there is no better cure for impatience than a few weeks in Andalucía. Antonio's brother, Rafael Chico, who acted as major-domo at the *Palacio*, always made a particular point of asking at what precise time we required breakfast and would repeat the specified hour carefully, as though impressing it on his memory. It was not until near the end of the expedition that I realized this was done merely to please me, for there was not a single clock or watch at the *Palacio* except our own!

Some of the more important work of the 1956 expedition is described elsewhere in this book. One of the many interesting studies of individual species was one carried out, chiefly by James Ferguson-Lees, on the Great Spotted Cuckoo. The familiar Cuckoo was uncommon, being chiefly a bird of passage, but the noisy Great Spotted Cuckoo was very much in evidence, though probably not more than thirty or forty of them were present in our study area. They tended to keep in small groups in localities near human habitation; that is, around the *Palacio* and the small white huts at Martinazo, Algaida, El Puntal, etc. We did not ascertain whether they were monogamous or, like the Cuckoo, polyandrous, though several males were often observed chasing the same female. The species they parasitized on the Coto appeared to be exclusively the Magpie. Elsewhere in Spain the Azure-winged Magpie and Raven have also been recorded as hosts; in Africa the Hooded Crow and several species of starling are chosen. Magpies are extremely numerous on the Coto, nesting chiefly in low bramble patches and thorn bushes, sometimes only just above ground level. Between 29 April and 11 May thirty nests of Magpies were examined in the hope of finding the egg of a Great Spotted Cuckoo. On 12 May James Ferguson-Lees and George Shannon made a further search and located seven more nests near the *Palacio*. Two contained young Great Spotted Cuckoos and three a mixture of the eggs of this species and of Magpies. The eggs of the two species were so similar that we realized we had probably been overlooking them. All the eggs were carefully marked with indelible ink. The notes made subsequently at these nests were most interesting and proved clearly not only that as many as three different hen cuckoos were laying in one Magpie's nest but that, as more eggs were laid, so the number of the host's eggs diminished. Moreover, on at least two occasions the addition of one Great Spotted Cuckoo's egg coincided with the disappearance of *two* Magpie's eggs. A further fascinating discovery was made. I quote from the record: 'On 12 May two of the Magpie's eggs in nest "C" had small dents in them. On 14 May one of these eggs had gone and three more were now dented. On 16 May two more of the dented eggs had gone, leaving two dented and two unharmed eggs of the Magpie.' Two questions arise. How were the eggs dented—deliberately or accidentally? It may perhaps have been accidental, as the nest was at one time crowded with a maximum of six eggs of the Magpie and five laid by three different Great Spotted Cuckoos. If the denting was deliberate, why were the eggs merely spoiled and not removed immediately? Again in 1957 we found two nests in which *only* the Magpies' eggs were dented. It was exciting to realize that the Great Spotted Cuckoos could not only recognize the distinction between their own eggs and those of the host, as one would expect, but also the eggs of other birds of their own kind, which they neither dented nor removed. In two nests examined in 1956 we found only broods of two and five young Great Spotted Cuckoos respectively; in 1957 we found broods of two, three and five, again without Magpies. In only one nest did we ever find the young of both species together, and this was for only a very brief period. The nest in question at one time contained three eggs of each species, two of those of the Magpie being dented. The remaining Magpie egg hatched three days after those of the Great Spotted Cuckoos. Two days later the nestling Magpie had disappeared, presumably having been either smothered or starved. Herein lay the crux of the matter, for the incubation period of the Great Spotted Cuckoo is only fourteen days, whereas that of the much larger Magpie is seventeen to eighteen days. Unless therefore the young Magpies can hatch out from eggs laid well in advance of those of the parasite, they can have no hope of survival.

In another nest, which finished up with six Great Spotted Cuckoos' eggs and only one of the host's, five of the former hatched over a period of three days, each having been incubated for fourteen days. The Magpie's egg and the remaining egg of the Great Spotted Cuckoo, which had been laid much later than the others of its kind, disappeared three days later, probably having been crushed meanwhile by the nestlings. It is evident that the parasitic behaviour of the Great Spotted Cuckoo is in many respects more complicated than that of our familiar Cuckoo, in which the single nestling merely evicts its foster-brothers from the nest. There is great need for someone to complete our study of this interesting and little-known bird.

In spite of this heavy predation, Magpies were thriving on the Coto and we found some fifty occupied nests in 1956. Their clutch sizes were on average larger than in England, some being of eight and nine eggs and one of ten. In 1957 I satisfied myself that Magpies recognized a potential enemy in the much smaller Great Spotted Cuckoo, by placing a mounted specimen of the latter near a nest which contained a mixed clutch of the eggs of the two species. It was at once mobbed noisily by the Magpies, which dived in turn at it, striking blows chiefly at the artificial eyes. Eventually one stood on the skin and hammered savagely at its head, finally knocking it from the stake to which it was wired. I then tried again at a nest which contained only Magpies' eggs, with identical results.

The eggs of the Great Spotted Cuckoo all bore a close resemblance to those of the Magpie, both in colour and markings, but on average were fractionally smaller and more elliptical, with redder spots. The fledglings were queer little objects, with greenish-grey upper parts, sprinkled with white spots. Their throats were rich buff and they had short but fully erectile crests. Their gapes were rather brighter pinkish-orange than the duller red of the young Magpies. As may be seen in Plate VI, there were often obvious differences in the ages of a brood.

Another interesting species which we had ample opportunity to study in 1956 was the Pratincole. On the night of our arrival we heard scores of these birds crying in the darkness as they migrated across the Coto. This northerly movement continued on and off by day and night until 2 May. Not all the birds crossed the Coto, however; large numbers settled on the Puntal mud-flats and on the bare islands in the *marismas*. As we rode among them we began to see signs of courtship, flight-chasing and aggressive display. We found the first eggs on 2 May. On 4 May three more clutches and many fresh scrapes were found. By 11 May breeding was in full progress and we continued to find fresh clutches until the 16th.

There was certainly no shortage of material when we began photography on the Puntal mud-flats. Nests of many species were so thick on the ground that one had to walk extremely carefully. From my hide at a Pratincole's nest I could watch the occupied nests of a Lapwing, a Kentish Plover, a Redshank and an Avocet, all within 30 yards. The Pratincoles were delightful subjects, with large, limpid dark eyes, neatly bordered creamy bibs and curious sealing-wax-red sides to their bills. Courting couples raced rapidly overhead on long, angular wings, crying their harsh '*kitty-kerrick-kerticktick*'. On the ground they ran very rapidly, like plovers, their disproportionately slender legs moving so fast as to be invisible. At each halt they bobbed their heads nervously several times. They are aggressive birds and squabbles occurred constantly on the borders of the breeding territories. Aggressive intention was indicated by lowering the breast to the ground, elevating the forked tail and spreading the wings wide on the ground. Lesser indications of aggression were shown by waving the wings slowly in a 'V' over the back, or by loosely flapping the half-closed wings, with the 'wrist' joints almost touching the ground. Pratincoles used all three actions repeatedly and very boldly at me as I rode through the colony, but they flew the instant I dismounted.

The courtship displays were more elaborate. One evening while I was in another hide the female began clucking and ticking quietly to herself and then left the nest and ran to a patch of bare ground, which I had already noted as a kind of no-man's-land between several adjoining territories. There she was joined by her mate and three other pairs, which proceeded to go through a remarkably beautiful sequence of communal displays, within a few yards of each other. The full sequence appeared to be as follows. First the birds of each pair bowed deeply to each other, their tails vertical and the white under-tail-coverts erected. They then stood face to face, perfectly still, with bills almost touching. This pose was held for as long as thirty seconds. Their heads then began to bob up and down, sometimes in unison, sometimes alternately. I was too far away to hear whether there was any vocal accompaniment. They then parted a few paces and began the bowing sequence again, but this time with one bird (the male?) opening its wings to display the rich chestnut linings. There were many minor variations to these actions, one of which was when the pair stood side by side, apparently actually leaning against each other, instead of standing immobile, bill to bill. It was a wonderful spectacle and the group of birds seemed to be enjoying mental stimulation on this neutral ground. The display lasted about ten minutes, the participants then dispersing in pairs to their territories.

We noticed that Pratincoles usually left their beautifully marked eggs untended during most of the day, returning to them chiefly in the late afternoons. As the shade temperatures at noon were usually between 80° and 90°F. there was little risk of the eggs chilling on the hot, dry mud, which was almost devoid of vegetation. Several birds laid their eggs on the tops of dried cow-pats (*see* Plate IX), which was possibly a deliberate attempt to insulate them from the fierce heat of the ground, though it may merely have been that the slight hollow on top of the cow-pat provided the right visual stimulus to birds seeking a suitable nest-site.

The mud-flats and islands were unfortunately overrun by cattle, horses and deer, which roamed the *marismas* in thousands. Our hides had an irresistible attraction to them as rubbing posts. Again and again we found that they had been knocked down and torn during the night. Had it not been for the skill of Lady Alanbrooke and Mariegold, who spent many hours mending them, the damage would have handicapped us seriously. In 1957 we tried the experiment of surrounding a hide with a barbed-wire fence. I was the first to try photography in the enclosure, which was a long way out in the Marisma de Hinojos. Alas for our hopes. Within an hour the first horse came ambling up to rub its neck luxuriantly on a corner post. I drove it away by shouting and waving my handker-chief out of a ventilator. It was soon replaced by five more horses, which I again scared away. An hour later I heard a deep breathing and puffing behind me. Cursing under my breath, I looked out of a peep-hole and found, within 6 ft. of me, a monstrous black and white bull. Shouting and waving at horses was one thing, but I drew the line at bulls. I kept silent and the bull began rubbing its tremendous neck on the corner post, which promptly fell over at an angle of forty-five degrees. It seemed to me that, finding no resistance, the bull must inevitably next try the hide in which I crouched. The exit was firmly pinned shut at the corner nearest the bull; the other sides were weighted down with heavy stones. My chances of escape seemed slender. Happily, at that moment the bull caught its foot in the barbed wire and shied away. By this time I felt I had tested the new device to protect the hide quite sufficiently and that discretion was the better part of valour. As soon as the bull was out of sight I struck camp and we did not try the device again.

Incidents such as this lent a spice of excitement to our work. Tree climbing and riding were other sources of mild adventure which some members indulged whenever possible. When the incomparable Pepe, our local tree-climbing expert, was with us our climbers usually remained on *terra firma*, as he could reach the crown of any tree bare-footed before they were half-way up the trunk with climbing irons; but James Ferguson-Lees and George Shannon climbed expertly and most of us had to climb occasionally. James Fisher, who is a very accomplished rock climber, disapproved of tree climbing; nevertheless, one scorching hot afternoon he was spotted comfortably lodged in the top of a large Cork Oak, fast asleep. When he descended, he recited a long list of birds seen, as someone unkindly put it, 'in his sleep'. He also firmly disapproved of all mules, having been the only member of the expedition to be thrown three times in the course of a single day!

Our work was enlivened during each expedition by the visits of two-man patrols from the picturesque *guardia civile* in black coal-scuttle helmets and green uniforms and armed with carbines. They passed through the Coto occasionally in the course of their search for smugglers. Smuggling has taken place from Tangiers and Gibraltar to La Linea, Algeciras and Tarifa since time immemorial and duty-free American cigarettes are still hawked freely around the café terraces in Jerez. One day I got into conversation with one of the guards who could speak a little English and we rode together for some miles. He told me he had recently caught a ragged peasant near El Rocío carrying a small fortune in gold wrist-watches, which had been 'swum across the frontier' at night by a trained dog carrying a waterproof bag on its back. My informant, who was a junior officer, was riding a particularly beautiful and exquisitely trained bay, of which he was obviously very fond. When I admired it he told me it was an English thoroughbred, which had until recently belonged to the London mounted police. Our ways parted before I could learn by what extraordinary circumstances such an animal had reached the wilds of the Coto Doñana. But it was in excellent hands and in superb condition.

The 1956 expedition achieved even more than I had hoped. We had studied the area in detail and had been fortunate to be present during a protracted migratory movement, details of which are given in Chapter 13. We had obtained a general assessment of the status and ecology of the breeding species and had made a detailed count of the complex populations at the heronries (*see* Chapter 7). The photographers and cinematographers had amassed a vast documentation on a long list of species, some of which had never previously been photographed. We had identified 171 different species of birds on the Coto, one of which was new to Spain (*see* Chapter 14). We were well satisfied. Yet, as we made our farewells, we realized that much still remained to be done and we began eagerly discussing the next expedition.

Soon after our return to London I learned what was certainly the happiest outcome of the expedition. Jerry and Mariegold had announced their engagement. They were married the following February.

Magpie attacking stuffed Great Spotted Cuckoo

XII *a*. The incomparable Pepe, who made a valuable contribution to the work of the expeditions. *b*. John Parrinder *left* and Antonio Chico discussing a problem of indentification with the aid of the illustrations in the *Field Guide to the Birds of Europe*

XIII   Charcoal-burning as practised on the Coto. The neatly stacked pine faggots are first covered with brush-wood, then pine needles and finally with sand, ventilation holes being left at intervals. Below is shown the final result and the *carbonero's* primitive home

4

THE THIRD EXPEDITION

O UR final expedition, in the spring of 1957, was the most ambitious of the three. We still had a number of important tasks to be attempted, notably to photograph the Spanish Imperial Eagle. This, we knew, was likely to present great difficulties, not the least of which was the transportation of half a ton of tubular scaffolding for the construction of the necessary high pylon. I was anxious this time to extend the scope of our work to embrace not only the birds but other fauna and the flora of the Coto Doñana, though these tasks would be given second priority. I wanted also to strengthen the ecological aspects of our studies, so that we might obtain a clearer picture of the relationships of the various bird species to the physiography and vegetation of the Coto and to learn how their survival was influenced by the obviously heavy pressure of predation of various kinds. Finally we wanted to investigate the adjacent *sierras*, from which the Coto draws, for example, its three vulture species. In order not to interfere with the main tasks, we decided that the advance party should spend a week in the *sierras* and that the rear party might also have a few days there if time permitted.

The composition of the team was designed with these various objectives in view. I again chose Eric Hosking as deputy leader and to direct photography. Lord Alanbrooke and George Shannon were obvious choices to be invited to join as cinematographers. I was very sorry that neither Roger Peterson nor Jerry Jamieson would be available, the former being in the Belgian Congo and the latter in New York at the time. James Fisher also was unfortunately out of the running, for business reasons. James Ferguson-Lees agreed to act as recorder again and to organize the field work. John Parrinder accepted the new task of sound recording, in addition to field work.

Seven new members were invited. Sir Julian and Lady Huxley agreed to take charge of the botanical study; I was particularly pleased that we should have the great benefit of Sir Julian's guidance on biological problems. As they could not stay the full period, Lady Alanbrooke very kindly agreed to continue the botanical collection thereafter. From the United States we recruited Reginald Denham, who, in spite of a busy life as one of America's leading playwrights and producers, is also an accomplished ornithologist; a strong point in his favour in our eyes was that he speaks Spanish.

To strengthen the field party I invited three expert ornithologists: my old friend Philip Hollom, who had already visited the Coto in 1938, Tony Miller and John Raines; the last-named, being a practising physician, was an obvious choice as our medical officer. The difficulty of finding someone who could undertake the very complex ecological work was solved by the addition of Max Nicholson; as Director General of the Nature Conservancy of Great Britain he could not have been bettered for this. There remained the need for a competent all-round zoologist who could study the mammals, reptiles and other miscellaneous fauna. It was essential that he should already be familiar with the animal life of Andalucía; such a man was difficult to find in England. On the advice of Professor François Bourlière, who is always in touch with an international network of mammalogists, I finally invited Don Antonio Valverde Gomez of the Instituto de Aclimatación de Almería. This brilliant young man was already well known to me as one of Spain's leading ornithologists and I was very pleased when he accepted. I assumed the minor job of collecting the entomological specimens from the Coto myself, having been promised the expert assistance of the British Museum (Natural History) in their identification. Finally, to complete the team, Don Mauricio González very kindly agreed to act once more as our

62

local organizer, with all the multitude of work which this entailed, and
to take part also in the expedition.

The advance party, consisting of Eric Hosking, George Shannon,
James Ferguson-Lees, Reggie Denham and 'Tono' Valverde, reached
Jerez de la Frontera on 28 April, where it was met by Don Mauricio.
Sir Julian and Lady Huxley joined a few days later. For a week the party
worked in the magnificently rugged country around Arcos, the Sierra de
Cabras, Algar, Grazalema, Ubrique, La Manga and the valley of the
Rio Majaceite. During this period the members sampled the hospitality
of a typical Spanish *posada*, or village inn, about which Abel Chapman
had written so feelingly sixty years ago. Plainly there had been no
improvement in the standards either of feeding or sanitation. The beds
were the nightly playground of regiments of voracious bugs.

Many interesting birds were seen by the advance party, among them
Great and Little Bustards, Bonelli's, Short-toed, Golden and Booted
Eagles, Rock Thrushes and Blue Rock Thrushes, Choughs, Pallid and
Alpine Swifts, Black Wheatears and Rock Buntings. Nests of both
Egyptian and Griffon Vultures were found among the high crags. It was
while the party was climbing a steep rock face to a cave in which an
Egyptian Vulture had its eggs that our first casualty occurred. Reggie
Denham lost his footing and took a bad fall, severely bruising both legs,
though fortunately without breaking any bones. A serious automobile
accident in America had left his legs particularly vulnerable to further
injury and this was the one hazard he had warned me he must avoid at all
costs. His knees began swelling alarmingly and he reluctantly decided that
there was nothing for it but to fly back to New York immediately for
treatment by his own doctor. He was bitterly disappointed and his loss
was a severe blow to the expedition.

Most of the remaining members reached Gibraltar by air on 4 May.
When we assembled for breakfast at the Rock Hotel, Tony Miller complained of nausea and pain in the region of his appendix. Realizing the
risk of serious illness occurring while we were on the Coto, a day's
journey from the nearest medical facilities, I sent him at once to the

British hospital for examination. An hour later we learned he was to be detained for observation. Following so quickly on the loss of Reggie Denham this was terrible news and as we set off for Jerez I wondered who would be the next to fall out. Fortunately Tony was released a few days later and was able to make a valuable contribution to our work, though he parted with his appendix soon after his return to England.

At Jerez we found as usual that Don Mauricio had everything perfectly under control. The heavy equipment and food supplies were already at the *Palacio* and the advance party had crossed the river that morning. Andalucía was suffering from an unprecedented drought and the *marismas* were almost entirely dry, so instead of taking our usual route we were to land farther up the river at Brenes. There two tractors would be waiting and would carry us over the dry bed of the marsh to our destination in an hour. By this means we arrived before the advance party, which had gone by the old route. Lord and Lady Alanbrooke arrived a week later, having been delayed by an unusual incident. The aircraft which they were to have joined at Madrid was put out of commission by a Kite which broke the pilot's windscreen, fortunately without causing a serious accident.

The great drought had far-reaching effects on the wild life of the Coto. Enormous areas of the *marismas* had become mere dust bowls. Deprived of their normally limitless breeding sites and food, large numbers of terns, waders, ducks and other water-dependent birds either were not breeding or were concentrated around the few remaining areas of wet marsh and on the saline lagoons and fresh-water lakes. Some impression of this concentration may be gained from the fact that we found flocks of as many as 400 Coots, 75 Black-necked Grebes and between 3,000 and 4,000 Mallard, and these were seen at the height of the breeding season! (The biggest concentration of Mallard was observed at El Hondón on 3 June.) Flocks of late migrant waders also tended to be unusually large because of the joining-up of various parties in search of suitable feeding places; for example, a flock of nearly 1,500 Black-tailed Godwits was seen as late as 21 May. A great host of predators, furred, feathered and reptilian,

XIV *a*. The shallow *marismas* extend for many hundreds of square miles; thousands of semi-wild horses and cattle roam across them. *b*. A corner of the Laguna de Santa Olalla, the largest of the chain of fresh-water lakes on the Coto Doñana

xv *a*. Setting out for the Veta de la Arena in punts towed by a mule. *Left to right:* James Fisher, James Ferguson-Lees, George Shannon. *b*. 'El Pitero' and his daughters entertaining expedition members outside their rush-built home in the *marismas*

swarmed over these restricted targets, in such numbers that the survival of eggs or young of any birds which attempted to breed appeared highly problematical. The thousands of birds of many species which in previous years had nested among the rich vegetation bordering the *marismas* had nearly all been forced to move elsewhere in order to obtain food. The big Bee-eater colony at Martinazo, for example, was reduced to twenty pairs, the remainder having moved partly to the mud-flats near El Puntal and partly far out into the Marisma de Hinojos, doubtless because of the lack of the dragonflies which form a staple item of their diet in the breeding season. In these new colonies every other nest-hole showed fresh tracks of rats or Ocellated Lizards seeking the eggs. The great heronries at Bellota Gorda and Santa Olalla were deserted and it was unlikely that many of the six heron species succeeded in breeding that year, though a few had begun laying by the time we left. The carrion-eating birds and big raptors, on the other hand, had life made very easy for them, the former by the plenitude of corpses of cattle and deer killed by the dearth of pasture and the latter by the concentration of their prey in accessible localities.

We felt the effects of the drought in a serious manner in another direction, for only one or two mules had survived, and although Don Mauricio contrived to hire tractors for us from time to time we remained very short of transport throughout the expedition.

Fortunately we had already studied the herons and waders fairly extensively on previous visits. Our primary objective now was the Spanish Imperial Eagle and we were overjoyed when Don Mauricio told us he had located a suitable eyrie with a newly hatched chick, in the Corral Quemado. Moreover, there was a nesting pair of Short-toed Eagles near Matalascañas. With two such important tasks as the photography of these rare species awaiting us we had little time to lament the drought, though the thought of the money and effort wasted in bringing our collapsible canoe for work in the *marismas* rankled for a while. Our ultimate success with the two eagles is described in later chapters.

The drought did however defeat our intention to photograph another very rare and interesting bird, the Purple Gallinule. This grotesquely proportioned creature, with its massive red bill, disproportionately large red legs and blue-black plumage, is extremely difficult to observe. It is not known to breed anywhere in Europe except in the southern tip of Spain, Sicily and Sardinia. We had not succeeded in catching sight of one during the two previous expeditions, though I had seen a few in Algeria. In a normal year it keeps to the seclusion of vast reed-beds well out from the shore, but on this occasion the drought enabled us to reach several localities where we saw Purple Gallinules at close quarters. The birds were observed opposite Algaida, in the channel of the Madre and at the Laguna Dulce and El Hondón. In spite of the water being heavily infested with big leeches, which were the bane of all our work in the *marismas*, the field party members were not content until they had found two nests. These were larger and higher than the average Coot's nest and had feeding platforms built near by. The surrounding *Phragmites* reeds and *Typha* reed-maces were about six feet tall and the water around the nests 15 in. deep. The eggs were as grotesque as the bird, being a bright pinkish buff, with irregular reddish-purple markings and ash-grey clouding, chiefly at the large end. They were slightly larger than the eggs of a Coot (55 × 39 mm., compared with 52.6 × 36.2 mm.) but were smaller than one would expect from so large a bird. The clutches were incomplete and were probably replacements after previous losses. The nests were again quickly robbed, either by Marsh Harriers, Jackdaws, rats or other predators which swarmed over the reed-beds. Some evidence of the feeding habits of the Purple Gallinule was obtained from the copious blood-stains on the platforms, which evidently came from leeches which had been eaten. We also found the remains of many beetles and part of a Water Snake, *Natrix maura*, on one of the platforms. There were large numbers of these snakes in the reed-beds. Another favourite food is the White Snail *Theba pisana sagittifera*, which is common in the *marismas*.

A few days after our arrival the barometer suddenly dropped and heavy rain began falling. For the first time during the three expeditions we were forced to spend a whole day indoors. The time was not wasted, however, each member being fully occupied with his own special task, or with domestic chores. In one corner of the room Julian and Juliette Huxley pored over the botanical presses. In another Tono Valverde extracted nematode parasites from the intestine of a snake. The field party argued fiercely around the table over a disputed record. Max Nicholson was engrossed with his vegetation maps, contours and water levels. Phil Hollom was quietly darning socks, his face a study in concentration. George Shannon and Eric Hosking overhauled a defective camera shutter. I occupied myself with sorting my miscellaneous collection of butterflies, beetles, flies and what the others called, unscientifically, 'just plain bugs'. To our varied conversations was added the distant singing of the pretty servant girls, whose musical peasant voices could always be heard in the kitchens. Our windows were open. On the heavy iron bars outside the one at which I was sitting, a row of five young Swallows were sheltering from the rain, barely 3 ft. from me; every few minutes the parents swooped up to feed them. Their loud, musical twittering filled the room. An almost white Gecko lizard sat motionless beneath the overhang at the top of the window, its widely spread spatulate fingers securely holding its suspended weight. Above me, under the high, arched ceiling, a Serotine Bat was flitting back and forth, occasionally making sallies through the open doorway to the dining hall. Looking around the spacious room, I compared the comfort we enjoyed at the *Palacio* through the generosity of our hosts with the conditions in Abel Chapman's early days on the Coto. During the very wet spring of 1883 he was camping out with one of the *guardas* and wrote in his diary, at the end of a strenuous day: 'Discomforts immense. Spanish tobacco. No meat. Strong dried cod and other nasty things. Everything wet and no fire, or chance of getting dry. No English spoken. Nothing to read, eat, drink, or sit on!'

The 1957 team was a particularly high-spirited one. Whenever John Parrinder, Max Nicholson or Tono Valverde were present, laughter was never long delayed. Tono's humour was that of an irrepressible schoolboy and extended to such things as apple-pie beds, as James

Ferguson-Lees learned to his cost. Max's humour was more sophisticated and he loved a play on words. The liberties he took with the Spanish and French languages were quite shameless. Tono spoke little English, but voluble French with a strong Spanish accent; our conversations with him were often a mixture of the three languages, all birds and beasts being identified in Latin. To hear him and Max discussing some obscure ecological problem in this extraordinary lingo was an experience unlikely to be forgotten, yet between them they produced one of the outstanding contributions to the expedition's documentation.

Julian Huxley's own particular brand of whip-lash wit also made its mark and reduced many a serious discussion to helpless hilarity. He is a superb raconteur. I am always surprised that people who do not know him often have an entirely false impression of an austere *savant* of almost terrifying erudition. *Savant* he undoubtedly is and perhaps one who may not always suffer fools gladly, but his infectious enthusiasm and ready laughter are completely disarming.

One of the notable characteristics of the people of Andalucía, and particularly those of the Coto, is their proud self-reliance. Not one of the *guardas* or servants at the *Palacio* ever asked us for any reward in return for the services they provided so willingly, though we saw to it, of course, that they were well paid on our departure. It was therefore with considerable pleasure that I learned of a way in which George Shannon could, without giving offence, help a member of the staff. One of the young girls, Paquita Robles, had severe toothache, and George, being a dentist by profession and having his instruments with him, extracted the tooth. Don Mauricio's wife, Doña Milagro, acted as an expert assistant and interpreter. The operation was performed in the monogrammed 'King's Suite', with the entire staff of the *Palacio* as a fascinated audience, though at a respectful distance. George remarked afterwards that he was probably the only dentist who had ever pulled the tooth of a peasant girl in a king's bedroom. It was a pleasant thought. Don Mauricio assured us however that dentistry at the *Palacio* was not always so easy. The *guarda mayor* of the Coto, the tough old Manuel Dominguez, had pooh-poohed

XVI Bitterns were numerous and were nesting in many parts of the *marismas*

XVII *a*. An Avocet returns to brood its eggs on the edge of a lagoon. *b*. A spectacular migratory movement of Black Terns was seen crossing the Coto Doñana in May 1956, while the local birds of this species were already incubating eggs

the notion of riding to town to see a dentist when he had a bad molar. Instead, he merely borrowed a pair of pliers from a tractor driver and pulled out the tooth himself. He then carved a new one out of deer horn, stuck it in the cavity with adhesive and was very proud to show it to anyone thereafter.

The *Palacio* staff, and particularly the girls, adored Doña Milagro, Lady Alanbrooke and Lady Huxley. Visitors were almost invariably men and the presence of the ladies on our expedition was a great source of interest. There was a delightful demonstration of this just before the end of the expedition, when Lady Alanbrooke had a birthday. At dinner that night the girls came in with a beautiful cake which the cook had made, on top of which they had stuck, in lieu of candles, twenty-one lighted tooth-picks! This was not all, for they crowned Lady Alanbrooke with a dainty head-dress made of the flowers of purple Larkspur (*see* Plate X*a*). The effect was quite charming and the gesture touching in its obvious sincerity.

The *guardas* and charcoal burners of the Coto were very happy and contented people compared with the miserable peasants often seen in other parts of Spain. I asked Don Mauricio whether they were ever employed in planting the seedling pine groves which could be seen neatly fenced here and there on the Coto. He replied that the plantations were the result of an interesting and almost feudal type of husbandry, known as the *rozas* system. From time to time a reliable peasant from the nearby villages of El Rocío or Almonte was brought to the Coto and given a short lease on two hectares of land. In exchange he agreed to burn the scrub, plough the land, sow it with wheat and fence it. He then harvested the crop, of which he was permitted to keep seven-eighths. The second year he sowed a mixture of barley and pine seed provided by the proprietors and harvested the barley above the tops of the emergent pines. The third year the pines were left to grow undisturbed behind their fencing and the peasant then started the same process on another plot. It seemed an admirable arrangement.

The happiest of the Coto's inhabitants was unquestionably Pepe. To us he was also a boon in every emergency. There was no tree he could not climb and apparently no load he could not cheerfully carry. For example, it had required two burly dock hands to lift Eric's case of metal pylon clips at Gibraltar; Pepe carried this on his back through ankle-deep mud when we were unloading at the river bank. Although small in stature his strength was that of a giant. He could throw a full-grown bull by running beside it, putting his hand beneath its throat to the opposite horn and jerking its head round. He offered to demonstrate this to us, but knowing that he had been injured once before while indulging in this sport I would not agree. He was usually bare-footed and would slide down a rough 20-ft. tree trunk as though it were a greasy pole; the calloused skin of his feet was so hard that he would not hear of putting on shoes to stamp out the embers of a camp fire. Almost everything we did seemed to him intensely funny and he roared with laughter on the slightest pretext. He, who could ride a bare-backed horse at full gallop without even a bridle, was convulsed with mirth when John Raines, who had never ridden before, failed to mount unaided a particularly tall pack-horse which had no stirrups. Pepe had an uncanny knack of anticipating our wishes and worked like a Trojan when we were building pylons, understanding precisely where to cut or tie a pole for maximum rigidity. His history was a strange one. He had been a sailor in his youth and drink had got the better of him. One day he asked permission to live on the Coto in order to stay out of reach of temptation and there quickly regained his health. He was supremely happy doing whatever menial task came along, helping the *guardas*, tending the charcoal burners' fires, cutting wood, or helping with the hunting parties. Although he had a room at the *Palacio* he nearly always slept on the ground out of doors. Occasionally he might disappear for a few days and go on a wild drinking bout at a neighbouring village, but this was now rare. His one deep passion in life was for animals and he would happily sit up all night with a sick fawn or Fox cub. His favourite *podenco*, a one-eared mongrel Greyhound, which shadowed him everywhere, was superbly trained and, although he might punish it savagely for chasing a deer, the bond between them was very deep. He talked to the dog constantly and could guide it with amazing skill to a running quarry by a series of different whistles. Often when we were riding across the scrub in a tractor Pepe would spot a Hare and would leap from the moving vehicle and race off, bare-footed through Gorse and Brambles, with his hound in pursuit. Five or ten minutes later he would reappear, the Hare dangling at his belt, and would vault up over the tail-board, triumphant, but scarcely out of breath.

Tono Valverde also was a source of some astonishment to us. In spite of being unable to bend his right knee, owing to chronic arthritis in earlier years, he was an excellent climber and apparently tireless. His knowledge of the Coto and its fauna, and particularly of the reptiles and batrachians, was invaluable to us. We soon became accustomed to seeing him casually picking up poisonous and harmless snakes, but his habit of producing frogs, toads and lizards from his pockets when we were having our evening drinks was sometimes a trifle disconcerting. He was completely fearless of animals, as was demonstrated by his encounter with the trapped Lynx, which I shall describe in another chapter.

Our work during the 1957 expedition was very varied and particularly rewarding. Apart from the considerable achievement of photographing the Short-toed and Spanish Imperial Eagles (*see* Chapters 9 and 12), we obtained the first pictures ever taken of the Azure-winged Magpie, Red-necked Nightjar and Spotless Starling. Other interesting birds photographed were the Fan-tailed, Savi's and Sardinian Warblers. In terms of cinematography Lord Alanbrooke scored another 'first' by filming a pair of the rare Marbled Teal feeding on the Sopetón lake. He and George Shannon obtained superb sequences of the Spanish Imperial Eagle and Eric Hosking filmed both eagle species. Among other birds filmed were the Egyptian, Black and Griffon Vultures, the Black Kite, the Hoopoe, the Woodchat Shrike and the Great Grey Shrike. A representative collection of the beautiful flowers of the Coto was photographed in colour and also most of the many snakes, frogs, toads and lizards.

An extremely competent investigation of the ecology of the Coto was carried out by Max Nicholson and Tono Valverde (*see* Chapter 18). This amply fulfilled my expectation that the area was likely to yield information of exceptional interest.

The field party, under James Ferguson-Lees, succeeded in identifying 204 different species of birds, of which 168 were seen actually on the Coto. Nests of fifty-eight species were found. Among the more important achievements was the identification of a bird never previously recorded in Europe (*see* Chapter 5).

I made an interesting study of the mobbing reactions of the Azure-winged Magpie, Magpie, Woodchat Shrike and Great Grey Shrike to the mounted skins of the Cuckoo, Great Spotted Cuckoo and Eagle Owl, placed near their nests. Some details of these experiments are given later. John Parrinder obtained many valuable recordings, including the first records of the voices of the adults and young of the Spanish Imperial Eagle and Short-toed Eagle and of the Red-necked Nightjar.

Our botanical and entomological collections were of great value in the ecological and ornithological studies. Both showed the fascinating influence of the geographical location of the Coto Doñana as an intermediate zone between the European and North African forms (*see* Chapter 15).

In spite of our initial mishaps and the devastating drought, the expedition returned with incomparably the most important and most varied documentation of any we had previously obtained.

Black-winged Stilt

5

BIRDS OF THE PLAINS

For all its wealth of raptorial birds and the amazing variety of its water-fowl, Andalucía must chiefly be famous for its spectacular Great Bustards, which, in spite of constant persecution, still roam the plains and farm-lands. Not that we in Britain can point an accusing finger at the manner in which Spain treats her Great Bustards, for by 1833 we had exterminated the last pair of the thousands which used to breed on the plains and wolds of England; the few stragglers which occurred thereafter speedily met the same fate. I had already had my appetite whetted by some slight acquaintance with various bustard species inhabiting India and Africa and was eager to see the noblest of them all, the Great Bustard, in its finest setting—the rolling corn-fields of southern Spain. Abel Chapman's enthusiastic accounts in his books about Spain were, of course, concerned chiefly with shooting and the trials of the chase of a bird which, even in his day, had become exceptionally difficult to approach. Though he shed many a crocodile tear while recounting how he shot no fewer than sixty-two of these great birds in a single season, his admiration for them shines throughout his writings.

A full-grown male Great Bustard, or *barbón* as he is called in Andalucía, can weigh as much as 35 lb. or more and is a magnificent sight, either on the wing or on the ground. Its head and thick neck are pale lavender grey. On either side of the strong, short bill sprouts a long whitish 'moustache' of stiff, back-swept bristles. The bird's back is golden buff closely barred with black, the under-parts snow-white, with a rich chestnut breast-band. In flight the long wings are chiefly white, with widely spread black flight feathers. The female is smaller and less stoutly built and lacks the 'moustaches' and breast-band. During the breeding season it is rare to catch sight of the females, as they are well hidden on their eggs in the corn. Breeding starts in April and the growth of the young coincides nicely with the increasing height of the sheltering crops.

My first sight of the Spanish Great Bustard was all I could have wished. Led by Don Mauricio, the 1952 expedition set off on mules and rode in driving rain across a great farm between Jerez and Bonanza, where a flock of males had been reported (*see* Plate III). On the way, an incident occurred which impressed us with the hardiness of the Andaluz. We were being guided by a grizzled little old man of seventy-one named Pelusa, whom Mauricio referred to affectionately as 'a confirmed poacher turned keeper'. His swarthy face was as wrinkled as an old boot, but the flashing dark eyes beneath the shaggy brows sparkled with vitality. As we were short of mules the old man rode pillion behind Mauricio, who is so tall that his long legs almost reached the ground on either side of the animal. Presently we came to a deep irrigation ditch. Mauricio's mule jumped it easily enough with its double load, but the old man, who was not holding on, was thrown heavily. Picking himself up, he told Mauricio he thought he had broken his shoulder. 'Nonsense,' said our host, though not unkindly, 'you just sit there under the tree and rest and I'll pick you up later on the way home.' When, later in the day, Mauricio rode back with him across the farm to the car it was obvious that the old man was in great pain, so he took him to hospital, where, sure enough, the broken shoulder was proved by X-ray. What he must have suffered on the ride can be imagined, but he made no protest. Needless to say, Mauricio, who looks after all his work-people like a father, arranged for him to be given the best hospital treatment and paid all the bills.

The keepers had reported a fine *bandada* (flock) of bustards on a hill-top. It is the invariable custom of the Great Bustard to settle on good vantage points where, even when the flock is resting, one old *barbón* always remains standing alertly on guard. After a long and muddy ride, with visibility badly obscured by rain, the clouds lifted and we could see mile upon mile of vivid green young corn, rolling away to the distant mountains. Our destination was an old well standing in a lonely gulley. The wells, or *bebederos*, of Andalucía, with their tall, rough-hewn, counter-balanced levers and white-washed stone walls, are exactly similar to those seen in the Holy Land and India. Here we dismounted and took up our position, more or less hidden. Mauricio and the *guardas* rode off in a wide semi-circle with the intention of locating the flock and driving it our way. It seemed a forlorn hope, as horsemen would be visible at a great distance.

Within half an hour we heard a faint shout and almost at once a flock of large birds appeared over the rising ground, winging straight towards us. All binoculars were eagerly focussed on them. Fourteen Great Bustards! They looked as big as swans and we were surprised by the slowly measured beat of the great wings, flashing white below and black and white above. The flock appeared not to be alarmed and soon pitched on a little rise some 250 yards away. We now had an opportunity to examine the birds in some detail. Their stout bodies were balanced horizontally on long, thick legs and their pale grey necks carried alertly straight, but slightly back from the vertical. One or two birds began feeding, making little pouncing runs as they snapped up grasshoppers. Others suddenly began displaying, with lowered heads, turkey-fashion, but with such elaboration that they seemed to turn their wings 'inside-out' and to contrive to look like great white chrysanthemums. Then the heads of the riders broke the skyline and the flock rose into the air, each bird first taking two or three running steps in order to gain momentum. To our joy they flew towards us, so that we could see every detail. Then the leader caught the flash of our upturned glasses and swerved violently to our right, taking the flock with him. As they swung broadside we realized that the deceptively slow wing-beat was amply compensated by its great power, which drove the birds 'whooshing' through the air at high speed. Nevertheless, had the redoubtable Abel Chapman been with us I have no doubt he could have scored an easy left and right as they turned.

It was a fine demonstration of Mauricio's skill that he succeeded in driving the flock so accurately over our small landmark.

Bustard shooting is, of course, still a favourite sport around Jerez, though the bags are becoming progressively smaller each year. It is not surprising that in a land of peasant poverty there is also a good deal of poaching, in and out of season. This takes two forms, so far as bustards are concerned. In one the poachers tramp the stubble fields in pairs by night. One carries a gun, the other a flashlamp and a small cattle bell, or *cencerro*. The bustards are accustomed to the tinkle of cattle bells and are therefore not alarmed by the shadowy shapes which accompany the sound at night. When a roosting bird is spotted it is held dazzled in the beam of the torch and shot where it lies. The other method capitalizes the bustard's need for water during the long, parched summer. The poacher takes up his position before dawn at a well, around which he has found fresh tracks of the birds, and merely waits for them to arrive. Sometimes he mounts a punt-gun on the well and gets a brace or more at a single shot. Even today it is probable that many more Great Bustards are killed by poachers than by legitimate shooting.

Nowadays shoots are organized as drives (*ojeos*), for it is of course impossible to 'walk up' a bustard in the open. Captain Collingwood Ingram, a grand ornithologist-sportsman who knows Andalucía intimately, gave a graphic description of modern bustard-shooting in an article in *Country Life* in the issue of 6 December 1956. In Chapman's day, at the turn of the century, a certain number were taken in the summer by putting a couple of experienced guns in a covered ox-cart, which was driven by a slow, circuitous route across the stubble towards a *bandada* of resting bustards, the driver using his goad on the oxen while lying hidden. This form of sport must have required an iron constitution, as the heat under a tarpaulin or raffia mat would have been intolerable. Moreover it is almost impossible to spot bustards once they have settled to a siesta in a patch of thistles, or Charlock, which provide the only available cover once the corn has been cut.

A small red beetle often infests the corn-fields around Jerez; as many

XVIII A Black-winged Stilt flexes her long red legs as she settles on her eggs

XIX   *a*. Two Cork Oaks supporting four White Storks' nests and many nests of Little Egrets and Night Herons.   *b*. A small part of the great heronry at Bellota Gorda, where 15,000 herons and egrets of four species were found breeding side by side

as 500 of these pests have been found in the crop of a Great Bustard. Although these birds make good eating, they have a curiously distinctive smell; we saw a peasant pick up a white feather, put it to his nose, and identify it as having belonged to a Great Bustard.

On our second expedition, although we spent a whole morning searching for Great Bustards on a farm where they had previously been sighted every day, they succeeded in eluding us. However, we had an opportunity to examine a superb breeding male, one of two which had been run down by a car while fighting on a farm road (*see* Plate III). We noticed that the bird had only recently moulted its primary wing-feathers, though it could obviously still fly without them. On our final expedition we were again successful in seeing another flock of males.

Although the Little Bustard is also a bird of the plains and farm-lands, it was in the foothills of the *sierras* that we first saw one (*see* Chapter 2). This is unquestionably the most beautiful of all Europe's game birds. Less than half the size of the Great Bustard, it has the same general form. The male in spring has a glossy, jet-black neck, with a lavender face and throat and two brilliant white 'collars', one running diagonally down the neck, the other horizontally below it. The crown and upper parts of the body are sandy buff, exquisitely pencilled with black; the under-parts are white. In flight the wings show pure white except for the tips, which are black. The female lacks the black and white pattern on the neck. Unlike its big cousin, the Little Bustard enjoys almost complete immunity from man, thanks to its extreme alertness, its willingness to lie flat on the ground when danger is near and to run in concealment before taking wing, and to its very fast, high and swerving flight. Not even the skilful Spanish sportsman ever attempts to drive Little Bustards, recognizing this as a hopeless task.

Little Bustards occur throughout a large part of Spain, in crops and low thickets and on the open plains among thistles and Palmetto scrub. A small flock was seen on the Coto Doñana, on a dry mud-flat, in July 1957. The flocks are compact in flight and the infallible Abel Chapman was able to boast of a chance double shot which brought down eight birds. The rapidly beating wings make a most distinctive noise, between a hiss and a rattle, which is clearly audible at a considerable distance. The Spanish name *Sisón* is thought to be onomatopoeic in its resemblance to this sound.

Next to the bustards, the numerous larks of the plains and farm-lands of Andalucía claimed our attention. They are a fascinating group and have given visiting ornithologists a good deal of trouble over their identification. I know of nowhere else in Europe where, with a bit of luck, one may see six different species in a single day. This happened to us in April 1952, in the plains, hills and richly cultivated regions around Jerez, where, in the course of a morning, we saw Wood, Crested, Thekla, Calandra, Short-toed and Lesser Short-toed Larks. Only the Sky Lark was missing, this being chiefly a breeding bird of the *sierras* in the southern part of Spain. The Lesser Short-toed is a fascinating little creature; it is sometimes called the Marisma Lark, which is a much more appropriate name, as it is essentially a bird of the dry areas of the *marismas*; it breeds nowhere else in Europe, though there are many other races of the same species, ranging from the Canary Isles and North Africa to Asia.

The Wood Lark and Sky Lark require little comment. They seem to prefer the mountain slopes to the plains and the Sky Lark has been found nesting in Andalucía at altitudes of up to 7,000 ft. We saw one or two isolated individuals of both species on the Coto Doñana in May 1956 and a few pairs of Wood Larks were breeding there in 1957 among the Stone Pines. Flocks of both species occur in the region during autumn migration.

The most 'difficult' pair, the Crested and Thekla Larks, occur virtually side by side in the plains and are common along the edges of the sandy mule tracks and roads through crops. We also found them in the sand dunes among pines on the Coto. After long periods of study in 1952 and 1956 we came to the conclusion that it was not possible to separate them with any certainty unless they could be seen together. When this occurred the Thekla's slightly thicker and shorter bill, darker and greyer coloration and more clearly streaked breast were apparent. It is also a very slightly smaller bird than the Crested. Although difficult to see, the colour beneath the wings when the birds are flushed is a useful field mark, the Crested showing a warm buff and the Thekla grey. However, both species tend to pick up the rich terra-cotta colour of the soil of the lowlands, so that a reddish lark with a long crest in these locations is not necessarily a Crested Lark.

It is obvious that when two such similar birds occur side by side and yet retain their specific identity, there must be some difference in their breeding ecology. We determined to discover what this might be and on our final expedition the task was given to our ecologist Max Nicholson, jointly with Phil Hollom, who has a wide experience of the larks of the Mediterranean region, from Spain to Turkey. Our hard-working field party, under James Ferguson-Lees, had already located some 'Crested/ Theklas', as we were obliged to call them in default of definite determination. These were in the Santa Olalla region and this was chosen as the study area. Within two days Max and Phil announced that they believed they had isolated a pair of each species and that these indicated a possible difference in breeding ecology. In a dune area dotted with clumps of *Juncus* a pair of crested larks with distinctly buffish plumage and long bills had been seen; the male sang during brief flights from the ground and showed buff beneath its wings. In another area, of stunted Halimium growing among sandy clearings, a second pair of crested larks had a territory. These birds had distinctly darker, earth-brown plumage on the upper-parts and the streaking on their breasts was finer and brighter than that of a typical Crested Lark. The male sang *chiefly from the tops of the bushes* and occasionally also while 'hanging on the wind' at heights of 30 to 40 ft. I examined this bird very closely through binoculars, at distances of down to 20 ft. As it alighted on the bushes I could clearly see that the linings of its wings were pale grey, with just a touch of buff nearest the body. Its bill was small and rather short. It was clearly a Thekla Lark and the other pair were presumably Crested Larks. We did not however find evidence that the latter were breeding on the Coto, and Tono Valverde, who knew both species better than any of us, doubted that they did so.

Other Theklas were soon found and in most instances their territories were among low bushes, from which they sang or took off for song flights, though some were seen in the dunes, whereas all the Crested Larks that year and in 1952 were in more open, sandy localities or in crops and were never seen on bushes. Final confirmation was obtained a few days later when one of the *guardas* showed Tono Valverde a lark which he had shot while it was singing on the top of a bush. James Ferguson-Lees and I examined the bird in detail. Apart from its distinctive coloration, the relatively short, stout bill and the formula of its wing-feathers clearly proved it to be a Thekla.

The call-notes of the Crested and Thekla are similar, a lilting and very liquid '*twee-tee-too*'. Roger Peterson and I found in 1952 that when both birds could be heard together over the corn-fields the Thekla's song was distinguishable as being a little less rich in tone and variety than the Crested's. Both songs are very brief and neither, of course, compares with the really splendid outpourings of the Calandra. The latter's song is richer, louder and more varied even than the Sky Lark's best efforts and it embodies Canary-like trills of great purity. The Calandra sings in high, circling flight as well as from the ground. Its call-note is a loud, rather nasal '*kleetra*'. This species is easily identified by its plump form, stubby bill, white rear-edges to its wings and conspicuous black neck markings.

The Short-toed and Lesser Short-toed Larks breed on the edges of the *marismas*, the dry mud-flats along the banks of the Guadalquivir and on the stony plains. Both are numerous, though the Lesser was very locally distributed, chiefly in the drier areas with denser vegetation. We noticed flocks of Short-toed Larks still moving about the Coto as late as the middle of May in 1956, by which time breeding pairs were already incubating eggs. The largest flock, of about 150 birds, was observed on 8 May. Without particularly seeking them we found eleven nests of this species in the Puntal region. These were in small depressions in or against small tufts of Glasswort or other stunted vegetation, only one being in a

xx *a.* Taking long-range pictures at the heronry, before erecting the hides. *Left to right:* Eric Hosking, George Shannon, Roger Peterson, Jerry Jamieson. *b.* Lord Alanbrooke obtained many unique cinema films of rare birds during the expeditions of 1956 and 1957

hoof mark, without shelter. Eight nests had a hitherto unrecorded feature of considerable interest, a little ramp composed of mud particles to the entrance, on the exposed side. The particles were mostly about the size of a pea, though a few were nearly as large as the bird's head. They had been collected from the crumbling edges of the cracks which criss-crossed the mud-flat. The nests had deep cups, neatly lined with fine grasses. All but one contained feathers, one having a large white Avocet feather placed like a sunshade over the entrance. The first eggs were found on 3 May. Other nests with incomplete clutches were found during the following ten days. There was no definite sign of breeding in the Algaida and *Palacio* regions at that time and it was evident that breeding in the *marismas* was regulated by the drying out of the mud-flats and islands, which in that region are the preferred sites.

It is sometimes difficult to separate the Short-toed and Lesser Short-toed Larks at normal observational range, as both have the habit of squatting very close to the ground while feeding. However, when the Short-toed stands erect its clear creamy-white breast and small dark neck-patches become visible (*see* Plate XI). The fine streaking on the upper breast of the Lesser Short-toed is visible when the bird is in an upright pose, and it is much the darker of the two in flight. The Short-toed can be recognized by its sparrow-like chirruping notes '*tchi-tchirrup*', whereas the Lesser calls a shorter, monosyllabic '*prrit*'. Both species have a high, musical little song of about eight quick notes, not unlike the twitter of a Swallow in pitch. We considered the Lesser Short-toed much the more musical and varied singer. The phrases are repeated in rather rapid succession for long periods. The Short-toed Lark usually, though not invariably, sings during a characteristic rising and falling song-flight, like the action of a child's 'yo-yo' toy. The song-flight of the Lesser Short-toed often has a similar character, but is less undulating. One of these birds which I watched at Brenes sang in close, rising spirals, alternately clockwise and anti-clock-wise, to a height of about 300 ft.; other members noted this on different occasions and it may well be typical of the species.

On each of the last two expeditions I passed pleasant days in a hide

XXI The beautiful little Squacco Heron displaying its golden-buff and pale amethyst-coloured plumes. The drooping crest feathers are black and white

watching Short-toed Larks at their nests and was struck by the immaculate whiteness of their breasts. Their short, stubby bills are distinctly finch-like. However, in their actions when running to their nests, their slender forms and long pink legs reminded me more of a pipit than a lark. Both sexes incubated the eggs and the male of one pair sang a pretty snatch of song from the nest when his mate came to relieve him.

In 1952 we had found a mixed breeding colony of Short-toed and Lesser Short-toed Larks on the mud-flats near the issue of the Caño de Brenes into the Rio Guadalquivir. They were again present in 1957 and it did not take Tony Miller long to find our first nest of the Lesser Short-toed. It was located in a slight depression against a tuft of Glasswort and contained four nestlings. Unlike the typical nest of the Short-toed, it had no feathers, but was lined with grass and fine bents. Plans were at once made to film and photograph the parents at the nest and to make sound recordings of the songs of the two species for detailed comparison. Unfortunately, however, a violent rain storm swept the Coto during the night and many of the nests on that part of the mud-flats were under water by morning. Nevertheless we had been able to determine one apparent diagnostic difference between the nestlings of the two species. Those of the Short-toed had yellow gapes, with five dark spots on their tongues, whereas the young Lesser Short-toed had orange gapes, with only three tongue spots. There is, however, still need for a great deal more study of these two interesting birds.

An eighth species, the very beautiful Dupont's Lark, *Chersophilus duponti*, has occurred in Andalucía, several having been shot at Málaga many years ago. It is a bird of the North African stony deserts, where I have observed it. It has a truly magnificent song and a characteristic habit of running long distances and then bobbing up from behind a stone or plant to watch the intruder. Its finely curved bill, long white eye-stripe and rather long tail make identification relatively simple. I prophesy that one day it will be seen on one of the dry mud-flats around the Coto.

I have always thought that other African larks must from time to time cross the narrow Strait of Gibraltar to the south of Spain. It was therefore no surprise to me when, on 3 June 1957, James Ferguson-Lees and John Raines had the good fortune to add yet another, the ninth, lark to Spain's astonishingly long list. This was, however, not an African but an Asiatic species, the Indian Sand Lark *Calandrella raytal*. The record was of exceptional interest, as the bird was new not only to Spain but to the whole of Europe. The lark was first spotted by John, who was attracted by its very pale grey, silvery upper-parts and white throat and upper breast. It was keeping company with a Short-toed Lark on the mud-flats at El Hondón and appeared noticeably smaller than its companion. John and James then kept the bird under close observation for three and a half hours, during which time it was minutely examined at short range with high-powered binoculars. Copious notes were made on the spot. No decision was taken about its identity until many series of skins had been independently examined in detail in relation to the written observations, at the British Museum (Natural History) and at the Liverpool Museum. There are two forms of *Calandrella raytal* and although the bird seen was more likely to have belonged to the western race *C. r. adamsi*, it was impossible to decide this, as the distinction from the eastern race is not apparent in the field.

An Andalusian bull

6

THE FABULOUS MARISMAS

THE wealth of wild-life in Andalucía is largely the outcome of an unusual variety of geography and vegetation. There are four main types of habitat—the high *sierras* (mountains), the *campiñas* (farmlands), the *vegas* (river valleys) and the *marismas* (marshes). The rich, swampy delta of the Rio Guadalquivir embraces a huge area of nearly 1,900 square kilometres, stretching from Sevilla in the north to Las Cabezas and El Rocío to the east and west and to Cádiz in the south. To the casual visitor the *marismas* may appear merely as a vast and indescribably desolate area of green reeds and tawny water, broken here and there by occasional patches of vegetation growing just above flood level. At the height of the long summer the water is sucked from the ground by the scorching sun, until nothing is left but mile upon mile of bleached, cracked mud and brown, parched reeds. In the autumn the rains come and the thirsty *marismas* return to their original state where, if one wished, one might again ride through the shallow water flanking the Coto Doñana for forty miles or more without setting foot on dry land. To the naturalist, however, it is a veritable paradise during all but the periods of extreme drought. In spring there is scarcely an acre of reed-bed which does not harbour nesting birds. The saline water itself is pregnant with living creatures, the hunters and the hunted, while every shore is starred with vividly coloured flowers and lush with aromatic vegetation. If the naturalist is amazed by the variety of the bird-life in spring, he is likely to be rendered speechless by the winged multitudes which pour into the

XXII *a*. A Cattle Egret raises its plumage before settling to brood its eggs. *b*. The distinctive, heavy 'jowl' and stout bill of the Cattle Egret are well shown in this picture

marismas, day after day, once the October rains begin to fall. Geese, ducks and waders from all parts of western Europe fill the sky with the rush of their wings, as flight after flight drops down to feed in the sheltered lagoons and to cover the mud-banks with an ever-changing carpet of multi-coloured forms.

Some impression of the quantities of winter wildfowl can be gathered from the shooting records compiled by Abel Chapman and Walter Buck during their frequent visits to the Coto from 1872 to 1912. For example, on 17 December 1905, Buck, with a single 12-bore gun, killed 235 Wigeon, 18 Pintail, 10 Shoveler, 6 Gadwall, 2 Teal, 1 Marbled Teal and a Grey Lag Goose—a total of 273 birds. In the early morning hours of 19 January 1909 he shot no fewer than 59 Grey Lag Geese. Chapman was not far from equalling his friend's figures, as witness his enthusiastic account of bringing down 'a perfect shower of Teal . . . from a feathered avalanche', some 30 birds falling from the flock to a left and right from his gun. The record bag from a single gun, working in the open *marismas* during one winter (1902–3), was also revealing:

Wigeon	277
Pintail	267
Mallard	9
Gadwall	21
Shoveler	195
Teal	276
Garganey	2
Marbled Teal	4
Pochard	1
Unenumerated	191
	1,243

One gathers that 'unenumerated' included anything that flew within range, such as Flamingoes, Cranes, Spoonbills, Glossy Ibises, herons and egrets, or eagles and harriers which came to chase wounded birds. Chapman confessed that his records were conservative, owing to the

XXIII Few birds can equal the beauty of the snow-white Little Egret's display

large numbers of wounded birds which he was unable to retrieve without disturbing the constant stream of fresh targets. Moreover, the list given above excludes birds of other species shot in the course of the season in other parts of the Coto Doñana.

More recent evidence of the density of wildfowl was obtained one evening in 1943, when Don Mauricio gave four cartridges to Manuel Dominguez, who was then the *guarda mayor*, with the request that he should try to shoot something for supper. Half an hour later he was handed back three of the cartridges and twenty-seven Teal which had fallen to a single shot.

During our springtime visits to the Coto and the *marismas*, the population of ducks was, of course, restricted chiefly to breeding species. We did, however, see a few tardy migrants (some of which breed in Spain) such as Scoter, Pochard, Wigeon, Garganey, Teal and Shoveler. We even saw small bands of Grey Lag Geese, some perhaps pricked or immature birds left behind by the winter flocks, though others were adults in fine condition; they were very shy and flew strongly. Mallards were, of course, plentiful, the first nestlings being seen on 6 May. Gadwall and Red-crested Pochard were observed regularly at Sopetón and at the Lucio del Membrillo and on the Santa Olalla lakes, where they were almost certainly nesting. Pintail are rare as a Spanish breeding species, but on 7 May 1956 we found a nest with eight eggs on the Puntal mud-flats; Tono Valverde found a second nest in the Hinojos region later. We observed a few of the dainty Marbled Teal in May 1952 and 1957, but none in 1956; they breed on the Coto in small numbers. Ferruginous Duck were noted on each visit and we were told by the *guardas* that they nest at Sopetón and at the Lucio del Membrillo; there were about twenty on Santa Olalla in 1957. Probably the species we most enjoyed watching was the curious little 'stiff-tail', the White-headed Duck; a few of these very rare birds were seen displaying on Santa Olalla and the Laguna del Saillo during May. The display consists of the drake swimming in front of its mate while jabbing its short, blue bill rapidly at the water half a dozen times and then jerking its head forward.

One of the most magnificent sights of the *marismas* is the Flamingo flock, which generally inhabits the Hinojos region during the spring, small numbers also occurring on the Lucio del Membrillo and elsewhere. These beautiful birds have been famous since the earliest recorded days of the Coto. They are, alas, no longer as numerous as in Chapman's time, but as many as 1,000 can usually still be seen. In the great drought of 1957, when the *marismas* were as dry in April as would be normal in August, we hunted for three weeks before finally locating the flock, which had been obliged to seek open water close to the river at the Lucio de los Ansares. All the earlier records are, of course, concerned with shooting—both in and out of season. H. F. Witherby, the chief author of the famous *Handbook of British Birds*, visited the Coto as a young man in the spring of 1898 with C. G. Chenevix-Trench and recorded his exultation as Flamingo after Flamingo fell to his gun. It is curious that a man who could write so lyrically of the Flamingo flock rising from the *marismas* 'like a flying sunset' as the birds spread their crimson wings, could also rejoice in slaughtering them. Abel Chapman, who shot far greater numbers of these birds year after year and boasted of bringing down four with one barrel, also described their beauty in glowing terms, but added the gastronomical after-thought that Flamingoes were quite unfit for culinary purposes and were in fact 'as tough as india-rubber'. Times have changed. Today most ornithologists hunt with cameras and note-books. Incidentally, it was in the *marismas*, in 1883, that Chapman first recorded the entirely orthodox manner in which Flamingoes dispose of their grotesquely long legs by doubling them beneath their bodies when sitting on their raised mud nests. Previously it had been thought that they either let them straddle on either side or stuck them straight out behind. Chapman's eye-witness account created a storm of controversy at the time.

In 1956 we studied part of the Flamingo flock in the Marisma de Hinojos at close quarters from a punt. Of the seventy-seven birds in a small group which was examined by James Ferguson-Lees only seven were in fully adult breeding plumage, with crimson and black wings

87

and pink legs, while eight were apparently nearly adult. Two extreme dwarfs accompanied the flock, one of which was in fully adult plumage; these were carefully examined in case they proved to be vagrant Lesser Flamingoes from Africa, which unfortunately they were not. We concluded that the flocks were composed chiefly of immature birds and perhaps also of old birds no longer able to breed. The breeding behaviour of Flamingoes is always shrouded in mystery and it is not uncommon for them to miss several seasons. Etienne Gallet has shown that young birds have been raised successfully in France's Camargue reserve only thirteen times in thirty-four years, yet the colony survives and at times thrives. When, for example, 1,800 Flamingoes died there in the great frosts during the winter of 1955–6, doubts were expressed that the colony could recover; but the following summer it produced the largest number of young birds yet recorded. Immature birds ringed in the Camargue have often been recovered in Andalucía, but Flamingoes have not been proved to have nested in the *marismas* since about 1941, when Don Pedro N. González Díez photographed nests with eggs at Las Nuevas. Without the aid of a helicopter, however, it is impossible to survey so great an area of marsh adequately. Such exploration might produce as great a surprise as did the now famous flight made by Leslie Brown in 1954 over the inaccessible soda lakes in Tanganyika. For many years naturalists had been striving to find the nesting place of the several million Lesser Flamingoes and Flamingoes which inhabit the East African Rift Valley. The local Masai tribesmen declared that these birds never laid eggs but sprang as young ones direct from the water! However, Brown searched the wild country by light aircraft and finally, on Lake Natron, spotted about 150,000 nests and young of the Lesser Flamingo and some hundreds of nests of the Flamingo. Later he nearly lost his life trying to reach the colony on foot, by walking over the soda crust which covered the nearly boiling water of the geyser-fed lake. His discovery was of great importance to ornithology. An illustrated account of this momentous adventure appeared in *Country Life* of 20 January 1955.

It seems unlikely that the size of the Spanish Flamingo population could be so well maintained over the years unless breeding took place at least occasionally. On the other hand the area may now represent merely an established summer feeding ground for non-breeding birds. Unfortunately the steadily diminishing salinity of the Coto side of the *marismas* may point to the eventual disappearance of the Flamingo, for according to research carried out by Robert Porter Allen, its food and breeding success depends on certain definite levels of salinity. In its established feeding areas it tolerates a fairly wide variation of 127 *grammes* (from 27·5 to 154·5 *gr.* of salts per 1,000 *gr.* of water). Major breeding areas, such as the Camargue, have a much narrower range of only 61·6 *gr.* and a much higher level of salinity (from 119·8 to 181·4 *gr. per mill.*). Whether any suitable breeding areas in the *marismas* still offer these conditions is a question requiring urgent study.

Exploration of the bird-life of the *marismas* presented us with a formidable problem, on account of the immensity of the area and the difficulty of moving about in the reed-beds and water. In 1952 we made an experimental penetration from the river, using a light one-man punt which could be poled equally well across wet mud or water. It proved much too strenuous a process to be recommended for long distances. Exploration by mule, or on foot, both cause a good deal of commotion, so that it is impossible to approach birds closely. Both methods are also hazardous, for, although the muddy water seldom exceeds 2 ft. in depth, there are many deep pot-holes and *caños* (gullies) into which a mule or a pedestrian can flounder headlong. The prospect of a ducking is not made more attractive by the presence of multitudes of voracious leeches, which can inflict deep wounds. James Ferguson-Lees, our most intrepid wader, often emerged festooned with these noisome creatures, establishing an unenviable record in 1957 with no fewer than forty-five attached to his legs and clothing after half an hour's wading; his trousers, socks and canvas shoes were stained bright red from multiple wounds, which, because of the anti-coagulant exuded by the leeches, bled freely for an hour or more. The ideal solution to the *marismas* is a canoe, which is relatively silent, manœuvrable and easily carried over mud-banks. We took a two-man collapsible canoe with us in 1957, but had no opportunity of using it because of the drought.

In 1956 we visited the little island known as the 'Veta de la Arena', which is located far out in the midst of the *marismas*. On a clear day its little clump of trees is visible from the *Palacio* as a blob on the horizon. As the whole party elected to go, Antonio Chico assembled a number of punts from the outlying regions. A motley collection they proved to be. Most of them leaked and two had to be bailed constantly. There were neither poles nor paddles. Antonio explained that we were to be transported in the time-honoured fashion of the *marismas*. The six punts were to be tied in two strings of three, each string then being tied to the tail of a mule. This may sound barbarous, but, once the little fleet was pushed off, the effort required to keep the punts in motion was very small. On 9 May we set out in high spirits. The height of the reeds prevented us from seeing many birds for the first hour, apart from occasional Marsh Harriers, but presently we reached an area of soft mud in the centre of which was a small island scarcely above water level. A group of cattle was grazing at one end of it. The punts were tethered and we stood ankle-deep in mud to see what birds we could find. Apart from the inevitable terns overhead—Whiskered, Black, Little and Gull-billed—the far shore of the island was sprinkled with waders. We counted 47 Knots, 15 of which were in red breeding plumage, 3 Turnstones, 3 Curlews, 20 Black-tailed Godwits, 2 Curlew Sandpipers, 4 Common Sandpipers, 2 Redshanks, a Greenshank, a Ruff, a Lapwing, several Avocets, Dunlins, Black-winged Stilts and a pack of various plovers which we listed as 23 Ringed, 1 Little Ringed, 7 Grey and 1 Kentish. Not a bad score for an island barely 300 yards long!

In parenthesis I might mention another good example of the richness of the bird-life of the *marismas*, which was obtained during the 1957 expedition by our ecologist, Max Nicholson. Taking a typical area of about 100 acres of barren ground and dry marsh, interspersed with *caños* and reed-beds, near Algaida, he counted all the birds he could see on or above it during an afternoon, taking care to avoid duplication. The list was quite staggering in its variety: 1 Heron, 1 Purple Heron, 60 Little Egrets, 1 Squacco Heron, 25 Cattle Egrets, 4 White Storks, 1 Glossy Ibis, 13 Mallard, 4 Gadwall, 1 Ferruginous Duck, 1 Egyptian Vulture, 2 Black Kites, 2 Marsh Harriers, 1 Quail (heard), 1 Purple Gallinule, 200 Coots, 12 Lapwings, 10 Kentish Plovers, 4 Curlews, 1 Whimbrel, 750 Black-tailed Godwits, 24 Redshanks, 10 Ruffs, 220 Black-winged Stilts, 150 Pratincoles, 100 Black Terns, 250 Whiskered Terns, 2 Gull-billed Terns, 12 Little Terns, 25 Wood Pigeons, 6 Bee-eaters, 3 Short-toed Larks, 1 Great Reed Warbler, 2 Fan-tailed Warblers, 1 Yellow Wagtail. This made a total of 35 species and 1,891 birds in 100 acres. Where else in Europe could such a variety be found, except perhaps in a coastal region during a migratory 'rush'?

To return to my story. The cattle splashed away across the marsh and disturbed the waders, so we turned our glasses on the open water beyond. In the distance were nine gulls 'up-ending'. One or two took flight and appeared to have an unusual appearance, with rather long necks and small, curiously hanging heads. The birds on the water also carried their heads tilted at a distinctive angle. They were Slender-billed Gulls, one of the rarest species in Europe. The only present-known western European breeding places are these *marismas*, and Sardinia, though there have also been a few records from the south of France. This beautiful little gull has a small, dark red bill, red legs and a faint rosy flush on its breast in the breeding season; in winter the breast is white and the legs yellowish. We saw more of these birds on the Lucio del Caballero and by the river on other occasions.

Having exhausted the possibilities on the little nameless island, we set off again through the reeds. Terns became increasingly numerous and soon we came across the first breeding colonies. There were a few Black Tern's nests with eggs, floating in about 18 in. of water, and about forty nests of Whiskered Terns, some tethered, others floating freely. Nearly all the Whiskered Terns had two or three eggs; but one nest contained a newly hatched chick and three eggs, while another had two chicks and two eggs. The colony was in two parts and we estimated that it contained between 400 and 500 pairs. There was another and even larger colony opposite Algaida. Apart from the four terns already mentioned, which are typical of the *marismas*, we suspected that Caspian Terns were breeding on the seashore near the Torre Carbonero. We also saw, during the last two expeditions, stragglers of four other species, the Common, Roseate, Sandwich and White-winged Black Terns. The last-mentioned, of which we saw five in company with Black Terns, on 14 May 1957, have very rarely been recorded in Spain.

During our journey we found eleven nests of Coots, four of which contained clutches of 10, 11 or 12 eggs, suggesting that the south Spanish averages are larger than the English. Whether the nests were of the common Coot *Fulica atra*, or of the Crested Coot *F. cristata*, it was impossible to say without seeing the birds, or knowing the differences between their eggs. Both species were certainly present and the *guardas* told us that between ten per cent and twenty per cent of the coots of the *marismas* were of the latter species. On another occasion we were able definitely to identify three nests of the Crested Coot; these were in the Laguna de Santa Olalla, where the sitting birds were observed from a hide and their curious twin red knobs either side of the bluish-white frontal shield of the bill clearly seen. The Crested Coot has a loud and almost human cry, 'hoo . . . hoo . . . hoo', and lacks the white which the Coot shows on its wings in flight. On our trip in the Marisma de Hinojos we also found two nests of Moorhens, with nine and eleven eggs respectively, and several nests of Little Grebes with large clutches. The most interesting nest we found was one belonging to a Black-necked Grebe, containing one of its own eggs and the egg of a Moorhen! We failed to discover any nests of that astonishing bird the Purple Gallinule, though, as I have recounted elsewhere, we were to find several on the following year's expedition.

By early afternoon we reached our final destination, the Veta de la Arena, where we were given a cordial welcome by the only family inhabiting it, Manuel Espinar and his wife and son and two daughters. Don Mauricio had told us that these people were content to live on this remote spot throughout the years, completely cut off from all neighbours.

XXIV *a.* Despite their long legs Little Egrets climb among slender twigs with great agility.
b. The much more heavily-built and rather slow-moving Night Heron has vivid red eyes
and three long, white nape-feathers extending nearly to its tail

It was immediately obvious that their little homestead was a happy one. The substantial one-storey rush hut, under its deep thatch, looked cool and inviting after the heat of the *marismas*. The living-room had been carefully swept and the hard mud floor was spotlessly clean. The best china was already set out on a well-scrubbed table and an exquisitely coloured Andalusian costume made by Señora Espinar hung in the open doorway for our inspection. In the roof-tree above the table Swallows were feeding their young in a nest, swooping in and out of the room, unmindful of our presence.

We had, of course, brought our lunch with us. When it was cleared away, Manuel Espinar invited us to sit outside on the shady side of the house to witness an exhibition of *flamenco* dancing. We had already heard of his skill on a home-made wooden flute, so accepted with alacrity. He was, in fact, known throughout the region as 'El Pitero' (the flautist). Few people knew his real name. Playing the flute with one hand and beating a drum with the other, he quickly demonstrated that his reputation was well earned. The two buxom girls, castanets in hand, danced gracefully for half an hour, with a complete lack of shyness which delighted us all. The cinematographers set up their tripods, while the rest of us applauded. A black pig, several hens and a perky Rufous Warbler emerged from the Prickly Pear hedge to join the admiring audience. Watching the dark-eyed girls pirouetting, singing and stamping their feet in the dust, to the accompaniment of the strangely musical one-man band, I reflected that here, in the middle of one of the remotest marshes in Europe, this charming family had found absolute contentment with their simple lot. When it was time for us to take our leave we felt our visit had been a singular privilege. There could be no question of paying for our entertainment, for our hosts had treated us as equals, with that proud but simple dignity for which the Andaluz is justly renowned. When I told Manuel Espinar that one of our members, Lord Alanbrooke, was a *Mariscal de Campo* and a *Vizconde* he gravely inclined his head almost imperceptibly, in acknowledgment of the information, but seemed quite unimpressed. We contrived to leave behind the balance of the food

xxv White Storks are seldom molested in Spain and, as this family group photographed on the Coto Doñana indicates, their behaviour at the nest is self-confident

and drink which we had taken with us and Eric Hosking later sent the family a collection of photographs he had taken during our visit.

On the long journey back to the *Palacio* we lay back in our punts and watched the sun going down over the reeds. The rhythmic *splosh, splosh, splosh* of the mules and the hissing of the reeds against the sides of the punts were soporific in the extreme and more than one of us dozed off. Only James Fisher and John Parrinder were kept alert by the water bubbling through the bottom of their craft; at one point there appeared to be as great a depth of water in their punt as outside it, so a halt was called while it was hauled out on a mud-bank for more reeds to be stuffed into the gaping seams.

As dusk approached, the frog chorus began. Bitterns boomed, grebes and coots clucked unseen around us. Overhead, strings of Little Egrets, glowing pink in the rays of the sun's embers, sailed towards land. A deep sense of peace gradually silenced even James, who finally lay right back in his water-logged punt, with a seraphic smile on his sunburnt face, and closed his eyes. We had seen perhaps one thousandth part of the great *marismas*, but it had been a most rewarding day.

Fishermen from Bonanza

7

THE HERONS AND THEIR ALLIES

Attracted by the inexhaustible food supply and the seclusion provided by the *marismas*, almost all of Europe's herons and heron-like birds occur on the Coto Doñana. Only the Great White Heron of eastern Europe is lacking. We found Herons, Purple Herons, Night Herons, Squacco Herons, Little Egrets, Cattle Egrets and Bitterns all breeding. One or two Little Bitterns were flushed; this species breeds elsewhere in the Guadalquivir delta and probably also on the Coto. White Storks are of course regular breeders on the Coto and there is still a small colony of Spoonbills just south of Huelva. Glossy Ibises and Cranes are seen every year and migrating Black Storks occur occasionally. A few Demoiselle Cranes used to pass through regularly on spring migration in Abel Chapman's day and a few have been seen since then. Finally, a flock of at least 1,000 Flamingoes spends the spring and summer of each year in the *marismas*. Of the last five species mentioned all but the Demoiselle Crane and Black Stork used to nest on the Coto; given continued protection they may yet do so again. The Black Stork, though rare, still breeds in parts of south-central Spain, and a pair nested just to the north of the Coto in 1952, but the nest was robbed by an egg-collector.

The main heronries are usually in the region known as Bellota Gorda, near Algaida. There is another mixed colony in the north at the Laguna de las Madres. In 1957 they were not occupied, on account of the extreme drought, though breeding was unsuccessfully attempted after our expedition left in June. The large colony photographed at Santa Olalla in 1908 by H.R.H. Philippe, Duke of Orléans, no longer exists.

As one approaches the heronry in a normal breeding year the blue sky becomes increasingly full of graceful white birds winging between the *marismas* and the breeding area. Flight after flight of snow-white Little Egrets passes overhead, their canary-yellow and occasionally red feet on long black legs projecting beyond their short tails. The pink and yellow bills of the more stocky Cattle Egrets are equally clearly seen. Night Herons, in sober grey, black and white, and the smaller Squacco Herons, with golden breasts and white wings, mingle with the throng. Stately White Storks, dwarfing all and as ponderous as ocean liners entering a crowded harbour, sail past at slightly greater altitudes.

The heronry appears on the horizon as a long white line, above which a veritable snow-storm seems to be raging, as thousands of birds descend to the heavily laden bushes. Drawing nearer, one becomes aware of a distant babel of voices, swelling minute by minute, like the sound of a vast children's playground. We dismount at a distance of 200 yards and walk through the scrub. Both sight and sound are now almost unbelievable. Every bush supports a dozen or more nests. On almost every twig a heron is balancing. All is movement and commotion. The birds take little notice of us and the air is filled with fresh arrivals, hovering as they seek a foothold. Every few moments there is a great roar of wings, as an excited group of a hundred or so birds rises, only to drift back again and squabble afresh for perching space.

We erect three hides along the perimeter of the colony. Once we are hidden inside, the noise and movement abate noticeably. From where I sit I can examine a dozen nests at close quarters. Almost at my feet are the nests of Cattle Egrets; on the left is a Night Heron on her eggs; to the right is a pair of Squaccos; in front, in a semi-circle, are the nests of six Little Egrets. The latter, I decide, are the noisiest of the group. Each time a newcomer alights, the Little Egrets half rise from their nests and give tongue. Not even in the great gull and tern colonies of northern Europe have I heard such a commotion, such a varied chorus of squawks, growls,

XXVI *a*. A colony of Purple Herons was found nesting in the rushes on the edge of the Laguna de Santa Olalla. *b*. Around all the fresh-water ponds the rich earth was deeply ploughed by Wild Boar seeking for succulent roots

XXVII *a*. The author examining a Barn Owl taken from a hollow tree near the *Palacio*.
b. Foxes were plentiful on the Coto; these orphan cubs were being reared by Pepe

grunts, clucks, caws and moans. Fights break out repeatedly, chiefly over the theft of nesting materials; they are spectacular affrays, but the blows seldom get home. A sitting bird reaches out its long neck and with its bill extracts a stick from its neighbour's nest; the instant this is perceived the owner rises with a cry of righteous indignation, erects the feathers of its crown and neck and lunges with its rapier bill at the thief. Every incident is contagious and bird after bird joins in until the whole group is involved in the pandemonium.

The greeting ceremonies are even more exciting to watch. As a Little Egret alights, with a twig in its bill, its mate rises from the nest and transforms itself into a miracle of pure, hazy whiteness by erecting the long feathers of its crown, breast and scapulars. The other bird does likewise, as it lays the twig on the nest. This is eagerly seized and woven into the fabric, with quick little side-to-side motions of the long bill. The birds then face each other and indulge in a chorus of deep, guttural bubbling noises, sounding like '*walla-walla-walla*'. The new arrival then steps on to the nest and pushes its mate gently aside. The eggs are turned and the bird sits, shuffling with its legs until the clutch is comfortably in position against the bare brood-patch.

The Little Egret, surely the most beautiful and graceful of the herons, only just escaped extermination at the hands of the plume hunters, at the time when women wore 'aigrettes' for adornment. Each year, in all the countries where they occurred, tens of thousands of Little Egrets were slaughtered while nesting, for the precious plumes grow only in the breeding season. Fortunately the stupid fashion died out and organized protection just succeeded in saving the remnants of the breeding colonies. Today the world population of the species is rapidly increasing once more.

All the herons appear to have some difficulty in selecting sticks of the appropriate length for nest-building. We obtained a fine sequence on our film, showing a Cattle Egret trying to take what it thought was a small twig from a shallow pond beneath the colony. The coveted twig was attached to a fallen branch some 8 ft. long, most of which was submerged. The bird dragged this for about 20 ft. through the water before it finally became entangled with some roots and had to be abandoned. Another bird carried a 3-ft. stick to its nest and succeeded after many efforts in weaving one end into the fabric. The other end stuck out at an awkward angle and got in the way of all the neighbours. For two days the pair did its utmost to dispose of the projection, going through the most ludicrous contortions meanwhile. It finally disappeared, perhaps by being stolen.

As happens in most nesting colonies, there was a good deal of sexual promiscuity between neighbours. On one occasion I saw a male Cattle Egret copulate with three different females in quick succession. There were other interesting incidents, as, for example, when a Cattle Egret walked across to a neighbour's nest when the owner was absent and solemnly punctured all her eggs! It is difficult to deduce reasons for such behaviour. Probably the constant nervous stimulation created in dense colonies upsets the mental equilibrium of some of the members.

One accepts the notion that colonial breeding confers certain advantages in collective defence against predators and that the bigger the colony the more difficult predation becomes. Certainly we never saw any attempt by the many big raptorial birds to raid the colony. The passage of an eagle overhead caused no alarm, though a few birds cocked their heads sideways to watch the sinister shape fly past. One evening we discovered a Spanish Imperial Eagle sitting on a tree in full view of the colony, but so secure did the herons feel that none made any attempt to drive it away. However, the herons certainly suffered from predation by egg-thieving Magpies and Jackdaws and probably also from four-footed enemies such as the Lynx, Wild Cat and Mongoose; the Montpellier Snake *Malpolon monspessulana*, which is abundant on the Coto and attains a length of 6 to 7 ft., is certainly another likely egg-thief. While in a hide one day I saw a Magpie working its way along the edge of the colony, helping itself to eggs from unattended nests, in full view of sitting birds, which scarcely bothered to turn their heads. Beneath the low branches in which the nests were situated the ground bore many fresh tracks of Wild Boar, which nightly took their toll of any eggs or young birds they could dislodge.

The Cattle Egrets showed great variation in the colours of their bills and legs. In the same group one could see birds with bills ranging from pale yellow to brilliant red, their leg colours being various shades of green, grey, brown, pink, purplish-red and yellowish. Some of the obviously breeding birds, however, had already lost their display colours and had pale yellow bills and dull legs. Some birds 'blushed' with colour at moments of sexual excitement, quite independently of the normal progression of the colour changes which take place over a period of some weeks at the beginning of the breeding season. More study is required on this interesting subject.

The Cattle Egret's head looks curiously heavy (*see* Plate XXII); this impression is heightened by the slightly pendant gular region, which gives the bird its characteristically heavy jowl, extending half-way along the lower mandible.

The distributional history of Cattle Egrets is a fascinating one. As their name implies, they have a habit of feeding for preference among cattle, which disturb the grasshoppers and frogs they are seeking. They often perch on cows, horses and deer to pick off ecto-parasites; I have seen them perched on elephants and buffaloes in Africa for the same purpose. Until 1930 they were known to breed only in certain parts of Asia and Africa and in the southern parts of Spain and Portugal. During that year ornithologists were astonished to discover that a small number had crossed the South Atlantic, from West Africa to British Guiana, probably assisted by a strong tail wind. The colony found ideal climatic conditions there and settled to feed among the Brahma cattle and presently to breed. It soon multiplied and in the following twenty years spread over the neighbouring frontiers into Venezuela, Colombia and Surinam. In 1948 two further discoveries were made. Large numbers of Cattle Egrets were found fully established in northern Australia, having reached that continent *via* the Malay archipelago. The same year the first Cattle Egret was also seen in Florida. In spite of knowledge of the South American colonies, it was put down to an escaped bird from a local zoological collection. In 1952, while Roger Peterson and I were photographing

Cattle Egrets on the Coto Doñana, we discussed the British Guiana invasion and he made a solemn prophecy.

'I'll bet we have Cattle Egrets in the United States soon,' he said. On his return home later that summer he was greeted with the news that they had, in fact, just been reported from three different states! The following year they were seen in six states. By 1954 there were no fewer than 2,000 Cattle Egrets in Florida alone, while state after state was reporting them. By 1957 they had spread as far west as Texas and vagrants were seen as far north as Newfoundland.

In the spring of 1955 I spent a memorable ten days with Roger Peterson and François Bourlière touring the Florida Everglades and prairies and we saw Cattle Egrets in many places. It seemed clear to us that the numbers were increasing annually at a greater rate than local breeding alone could provide and that reinforcements from elsewhere must be making up the balance. After my long familiarity with the species in three other continents it was difficult to realize that I was witnessing one of the most remarkable events in recent ornithology. A fine account of the American invasion is given in Peterson and Fisher's *Wild America*.

An even more dramatic event in connection with the distribution of the Cattle Egret occurred while I was writing this book. A nestling Cattle Egret, ringed on the Coto in the summer of 1956 by Tono Valverde, was recovered in Trinidad in the spring of 1957. The distance by direct flight is about 4,000 miles. If, as is probable, the bird travelled *via* West Africa and the Cape Verde Islands before crossing the South Atlantic, the distance would have been much greater. This recovery is one of the most important yet obtained since the ringing of wild birds began, and it provides the first definite proof of the ability of this species to fly from Europe to the Americas.

We had an excellent opportunity in the Bellota Gorda colony to study the Squacco Heron, a species about which very little was yet known. It had not, I believe, previously been photographed in colour, nor filmed at the nest. In its breeding plumage it is a strikingly beautiful bird. In display it rivals the Little Egret in grace. Its long, amethyst-

XXVIII *a*. Red Deer fawns were often found hiding in the scrub; unfortunately Lynxes kill many of them during May and June. *b*. Herds of Fallow Deer were numerous in the grassy clearings around the lakes and were much less shy than the Red Deer

XXIX *Above:* The tiny emerald-green Canary Islands Hyla, or Tree Frog, and the introduced Greek Tortoise. *Below:* The Southern Mud Frog and the prehensile-toed Moorish Gecko

coloured scapular 'cloak' and the rich golden-buff throat and breast feathers make an enchanting impression when erected, transforming the displaying bird into a misty globe of pastel shades. The narrow, pointed feathers of the drooping crest are white, narrowly bordered with black. Perhaps the most striking feature is the coloration of the bill, which at the beginning of the breeding season is a clear cobalt blue. Soon afterwards the bill develops a blackish tip and a grey centre, eventually reverting to the normal winter colour of yellowish green with a dark tip. During the breeding season the bare skin between the bill and the piercing lemon-yellow eyes is a startling emerald green. The head is small and very narrow, giving a distinctly serpentine impression when seen from the front. The legs also are subject to seasonal changes of colour, being coral red at the beginning of May, thereafter fading to yellowish green.

The Night Herons were always the least active and least vocal birds in the colony, as might be expected from their normally crepuscular habit. One gained the impression that they were the social *élite*, disdaining contact with their garrulous neighbours. Their movements were slow and very deliberate as they clambered by easy stages to their nests, pausing from time to time in a peculiarly statuesque manner, often with one foot outstretched to grasp the next branch. Once on their nests they were immobile, with the exception of the loose skin of their throats, which flickered as they panted in the gruelling heat. Their large, protuberant eyes, crimson as rubies and set in a patch of bare, blue-grey skin, missed nothing of the changing scene around them. The colour of their legs varies from dull crimson in the breeding season to yellowish green or yellowish grey in winter. To casual observation the Night Heron's back is dull black; in bright sunlight it shines with a magnificent bottle-green gloss, over which the three long, white nape feathers droop nearly to its tail.

It was important to us in 1956 to make a census of the breeding birds of the four species in the main colony. The task presented appalling difficulties, as it was impossible to penetrate the tangled vegetation without upsetting nests and eggs. Moreover many hundreds of non-breeding birds were constantly present in the ceaselessly changing throng.

Fortunately James Fisher is an expert in counting sea-bird colonies and he appeared undaunted by the new task. After surveying the terrain, he and James Ferguson-Lees set about the job methodically. Sample counts were made at different times of day and from different angles. The results were cross-checked and 'grossed-up' statistically. The grand totals, reached independently, showed a difference of only about one per cent. In view of the difficulty of clearly distinguishing the species precisely through the dense jungle of twigs, we were greatly impressed.

The colony was in three parts, which for convenience we named 'A', 'B' and 'C'. Colonies 'A' and 'B' were known to us from the 1952 expedition; colony 'C', which was larger than the other two, was evidently established since our first visit.

On 29 April a trial count was made of colonies 'A' and 'B'. This showed that 'A' contained about 500 occupied nests of Little Egrets, 400 of Cattle Egrets, 100 of Night Herons and 5 pairs of Squacco Herons apparently preparing to nest. (In all the colonies the Squacco bred later than the other herons.) There were in addition some 300 to 400 non-breeding and immature birds of the four species, clambering about among the old and new nests. Colony 'B' at that time contained about 500 to 600 occupied nests of Little Egrets, 1,200 of Cattle Egrets, 50 of Night Herons and 10 to 15 pairs of Squacco Herons preparing to breed. Again there were several hundred non-breeding birds present.

Between 5 and 10 May colony 'A' was severely robbed by peasant poachers. The birds deserted *en masse* and moved to colony 'C'. The final census for that year, made on 15 May, gave the following maximum and minimum estimates for *occupied* nests. Fisher's figures are shown in the left-hand columns and Ferguson-Lees's on the right:

	Colony 'A'	Colony 'B'	Colony 'C'	Totals
Little Egret	12/12	400/ 550	2400/2800	2810/3360
Cattle Egret	—	1600/1300	470/ 500	2070/1800
Night Heron	—	70/ 60	1870/1700	1940/1760
Squacco Heron	—	20/ 20	70/ 40	90/ 60
	12/12	2090/1930	4810/5040	6910/6980

Counting two birds to each nest and adding a conservative margin for non-breeding and immature birds, we calculated that the total numbers of birds of the four species in the three colonies was at least 15,000. By the time the young left the nests that summer the figure would certainly be at the very least doubled. These figures exclude the mixed colony found by Eric Simms[1] at the Laguna de las Madres that year, which contained a further ninety breeding pairs.

Some interesting indications are now becoming available concerning the post-breeding dispersal of the herons and egrets of the Coto, thanks to the activities of Spain's enthusiastic Aranzadi ringing team. By 1956 they had ringed some 7,000 of these birds as nestlings. Little Egrets ringed on the Coto have been recovered by September of the same year in Portugal, Italy, Morocco and the Canary Isles. Cattle Egrets have provided fewer recoveries; these seem to show that by November dispersal is chiefly to south-east Spain and Portugal, though the species is known to migrate also from the Coto to Morocco. R. E. Moreau has pointed out that the lack of ringing recoveries from North Africa is doubtless connected with the Muslim's disinclination to molest birds which accompany his cattle. The Night Heron recoveries indicate a much more rapid dispersal, though not beyond Spain and Portugal, the only distant recovery being of a bird which was killed in northern Italy fourteen months later.

The extraordinary breeding concentration of different species of herons, probably the biggest in Europe, which occurs on the Coto Doñana would be impossible if there were active competition for the same kind of food. Tono Valverde made a study during several seasons of the food given to their nestlings. This showed that competition is in fact slight, moreover that the foraging ranges are not only very large, but do not necessarily overlap. The chief feeding grounds of the Little and Cattle Egrets and the Night Herons were proved to cover a radius of up to fifteen miles from the colony, while the Squacco Herons ranged up to six miles for food, often in localities where the other species rarely

---

[1] Eric Simms was not a member of the expedition, but was working independently near the Coto, making sound recordings for the BBC natural history unit.

occurred. The Cattle Egrets, which chiefly eat insects and small vertebrates, take very few fish, but the other small herons are very fond of
the plump *Carassius*, a very abundant fish of the *marismas*. Little Egrets
eat large numbers of the little *Gambusia* fish, which was introduced only
recently into Spain to control mosquito larvae. Night Herons have a
liking for toads and eels, as well as the *Carassius* fish. Squacco Herons eat
big quantities of aquatic insects and some fish. By tracing the sources of
the food given to nestlings it was possible to prove, for example, that the
Little Egrets and Night Herons foraged along the banks of the Guadalquivir for fish species such as *Mugil* and *Atherina*, which do not occur in
the *marismas*. These differences in feeding habitats, and particularly of the
dispersal caused by the drought, were most marked in 1957. Almost the
entire Squacco population remained visible on the Coto. Cattle Egrets
were present in good numbers. Little Egrets were less numerous and
Purple Herons were much reduced. Night Herons, of which we had
seen some 4,000 in 1956, were observed fewer than a dozen times.

Near the northern boundary of colony 'A' there was a group of
ancient Cork Oaks, some dying of old age, others long since reduced to
mere skeletons or stumps. In the crowns of the living trees we found seven
occupied nests of the familiar grey Heron. Later, when this colony was
deserted by the smaller herons, these nests also were abandoned. Shortly
afterwards, near colony 'C', forty pairs of Herons were discovered nesting
in the only two substantial trees, which were again Cork Oaks. Doubtless
the birds from colony 'A' were among them. Eric Simms found a further
group of ten breeding pairs at the Laguna de las Madres. These were the
only nests of this species we found that year; but in view of the large
number of Herons observed feeding in the *marismas* we judged that there
must be another, as yet undiscovered, breeding colony elsewhere in the
area. In 1957 only twenty pairs of Herons attempted to breed and even
these soon deserted because of the drought. The Herons were on good
terms with the White Storks, which nested near them. We often saw
them together, indulging in very high soaring flight. One evening I was
watching a Heron feeding in a lagoon when it suddenly put back its head

and gave a loud, croaking cry. Looking up, I spied a solitary Heron wheeling overhead in a thermal current, at such a height that it was scarcely distinguishable with the naked eye. But the Heron in the lagoon had quite obviously recognized it. On another occasion I was interested to see eight Herons flying in perfect 'V' formation, like geese, which I do not believe has been recorded before.

Counting the occupied nests of the White Storks appeared a simple task, but we soon realized that non-breeding birds often sat for long periods on old nests, in a most determined manner. In 1952 we found twelve occupied nests; in 1956 there were seventeen; in 1957 there were only eleven. However, it was again evident that the total population of storks in the *marismas* was far larger than could be calculated from the nests and that a considerable number of non-breeding birds was always present. The nests were vast, solid structures, some of them seven feet in depth with the accumulated architecture of succeeding generations. One great tree containing three nests was thought to be recognizable as the one portrayed in Abel Chapman's book. Two nests were on stumps no higher than 9 or 10 ft. from the ground. At one of these I spent many hours watching a battle royal between a pair of Jackdaws and a pair of Green Woodpeckers, for possession of a hole which the latter had just excavated 2 ft. below the stork's nest. The stork drowsed with her eyes closed, oblivious of the bitter struggle. Again and again the woodpeckers threw out the Jackdaws' sticks, but the moment the hole was vacated a Jackdaw popped in. Sometimes all four birds clung to the stump, chattering and screaming at each other. The Jackdaws, as usual, finally won. The Spanish race of the Green Woodpecker *Picus viridis sharpei* was clearly distinguishable from the British race, both by its coloration and its voice. It looked greyer and there was a vinous tinge to its cheeks. Less easily seen were the un-barred under-tail-coverts and the smaller areas of black on the face. The ringing cry or 'yaffle' sounded deeper in tone and slower in delivery, each note resembling '*chock*' rather than the familiar '*chack*' of our bird. The species is common on the Coto, though the increasing competition of the Jackdaws for the nest-holes offers

a serious threat, as indeed it does to the Hoopoes, Rollers, Little Owls and
other species which nest in holes. Jackdaws have multiplied on the Coto
to such an extent in recent years as to represent a major problem in the
conservation of many other species. They prey heavily on the eggs of
the various herons, among which they breed in hundreds. Nearly all the
storks' nests had Jackdaws in the foundations. Every time the heron
colonies were disturbed, swarms of Jackdaws could be seen taking eggs.
Almost all the Cork Oaks on the Coto contained at least one pair in their
cavities, or in old storks' nests, or in holes under the roots. A pair of
Jackdaws was even found with a nest 26 ft. below ground, in a well near
the Torre Carbonero.

To revert to the White Storks; it was, of course, their very elaborate
greeting ceremonies which interested us most. The ritual, which is
maintained until the young are about to leave the nest, apparently
provides a source of great satisfaction and stimulation to the birds and as
often as not the whole sequence is gone through twice at each greeting.
In 1957 we even observed a bird clappering in flight at an altitude of
200 ft.; it dropped its legs momentarily but otherwise maintained a
normal flying attitude. The ceremony at the nest takes place as follows.
The sitting bird spies her mate approaching and evidently is able to recognize him in flight at about 200 yards. She raises her head and lets out a
deep squawk of welcome. As he alights on the nest she rises to face him.
Both then throw their heads right back towards their tails and begin a
rapid clappering with their bills. The sound is like that of a very resonant
kettle drum and is audible for half a mile. Their small crimson throat-
pouches are inflated in order to increase the resonance. The birds then
bow their heads towards each other, still clappering vigorously, and half
open their wings, swaying their bodies slowly from side to side meanwhile. The clappering then dies down and, unless the ceremony is to be
repeated, the birds parade slowly around the nest until they have changed
places. The relieved bird then flies and its mate turns the eggs and settles
down to brood, or to feed the young. The newly hatched nestlings are
charming little creatures, with woolly white down and short black bills.

The literature on the White Stork says very little about its roosting behaviour. During the 1957 expedition Sir Julian Huxley drew our attention to this fact when he noticed that a small number of storks roosted in an Elm on the edge of the *marismas*. Our rear party, however, made a startling discovery of 400-450 White Storks which had established a communal roost in an Olive grove near El Bujón, not far from Jerez. Some of the trees were already ruined by the accumulated excreta, but the proprietor of the grove fortunately was a bird lover and said he was quite willing to lose a few trees for the pleasure of seeing this great concourse of storks assemble each evening. Unfortunately our rear party had time neither to ascertain from how far afield the roosting birds came, nor how long the roost had been established. It is incidentally interesting that the region of the *marismas* is the only place in Spain where White Storks frequently remain throughout the winter, instead of migrating.

At the Laguna Dulce, some miles west of the *Palacio*, there is a long-established breeding colony of Purple Herons. In 1952 it contained only about twenty pairs, with a common Heron nesting in the reeds among them. In 1956, however, we counted at least forty occupied nests there and Eric Simms found a further five by the Laguna de las Madres. There was another colony at El Higuerón. All were in tall *Phragmites* close to deep water. On 3 May most of the Laguna Dulce nests contained complete clutches, the maximum being seven eggs. On 13 May the first nestlings were heard calling for food. Hides were put up on two nests and Lord Alanbrooke, Roger Peterson and George Shannon all obtained good film sequences, while Eric Hosking contented himself with some stills. The birds behaved well, sunning themselves, preening and exercising their long, snake-like necks, to the delectation of the photographers. The Purple Heron is a handsome creature and its rich chestnut and purplish-grey plumage made a striking picture against the blue water. When standing alarmed and erect, the full value of the vertical stripes of white, black and chestnut on the thin, serpentine neck was instantly apparent in its close resemblance to the light and shade on the reeds. Like all its relatives, the Purple Heron suffered severely from egg predation by the numerous Magpies. Many nests were robbed and Roger only just saved the clutch he was photographing by shouting at a Magpie which was in the very act of breaking an egg. He recorded the incident in his film.

In order to count the Purple Herons' nests it was obviously wise to take to the water, for fear of trampling the reed-beds. James Ferguson-Lees, being one of the more athletic members of the expedition, was detailed to swim around the lake. He cheerfully stripped and plunged in. The water was warm and some of the others present, perspiring after their long ride, looked envious as he splashed about. However, when he returned and clambered out, he was seen to be streaming with blood from half a dozen severe leech bites. Amid cries of surprise and excitement, one of the photographers was heard urgently exclaiming: 'Don't pick the leeches off! First take his picture in glorious Technicolor!'

So far as we could learn, none of the Purple Herons succeeded in breeding in 1957.

White Storks' greeting ceremony

xxx   *a.* The Water Snake was the commonest species on the Coto and was the chief food of the Short-toed Eagle.   *b.* The Ladder Snake was easily recognized by the cross-barring on its back, from which it gets its name. Both species are non-poisonous

XXXI *Above:* The Ocellated, or Eyed, Lizard attains a length of 3 ft. and can kill Rabbits.
Centre: The Algerian Sand Lizard. *Below:* The Spine-foot Lizard

8

WILD ANIMALS OF THE COTO

ALTHOUGH the Coto Doñana has served as a ducal hunting reserve for hundreds of years and continues to this day to provide sport on a properly controlled basis for its present owners, its animal life still thrives in scarcely diminished abundance. Except for minor changes in vegetation, the region and its wild life appear to be just as they were at the time of Felipe IV's visit in 1624, as described in the Duke of Almázan's fascinating *Historia de la Monteria en España*. No mammal species has been lost since records were first compiled. The list is a long one and astonishingly varied for so small an area, which, moreover, is without either forests or hills, much less mountains.

The chief attraction to the hunting fraternity has, of course, always been the noble Red Deer. It is smaller than the northern European race and has no mane. Because of the poor pasturage the stags seldom attain the dimensions of those in the Sierra Morena, which are probably the largest in Spain, but they are well proportioned and twelve or even fourteen points are occasionally seen. The Coto is the only place in Spain where Red Deer live permanently in a lowland area. Fallow Deer, which are thought to have been introduced into the Iberian peninsula by the Romans, are also numerous, but are nowadays seldom hunted. The combined populations of the two species at the time of our last visit were between 1,500 and 2,000. The Red Deer keep chiefly to the Halimium and Tree Heath regions, feeding at night in the grassy clearings and among the trees, while the Fallow Deer, which are much less retiring, prefer the Bracken- and grass-covered borders of the *marismas* and lakes. Apart from human hunters and poachers, neither species has to fear any local enemy, though both suffer considerable losses of their young to the Lynx. Wolves from the *sierras* to the north very occasionally descend to the Coto and play temporary havoc with the deer, but they cannot escape the vigilance of the watchful *guardas* for long. The last Wolf raider, an immense animal, was shot in February 1953.

We came across a number of fawns of both deer species and their delightful appearance never failed to bring about a temporary lull in ornithology. If we surprised them feeding with their dams the latter quickly galloped out of sight; the fawns generally ran unsteadily for a hundred yards or so and then flopped down and lay motionless. We could then walk up to them and even stroke them without their moving a muscle (*see* Plate XXVIII). If picked up, however, they struggled and cried loudly, with piercing and very human screams.

The next animal of importance to the hunter on the Coto is probably the redoubtable Wild Boar, of which there are usually some thousands. Every few years, however, swine fever strikes the region and almost wipes out the population. This happened in the winter of 1956 and we saw only five Wild Boar during the whole of the following May. In previous years the borders of the *marismas* and every boggy hollow throughout the Coto were deeply ploughed and re-ploughed, as though by mighty machines, by the strong snouts of these animals in search of the roots or tasty Mole Crickets of which they are so passionately fond. These rootings become seed-beds for the germination of new vegetation; Wild Boar thus contribute importantly to the spread of plant life. At dawn and dusk we often observed small parties trotting off at our approach; occasionally we disturbed them at their daytime resting places among the undergrowth and they went crashing away at top speed, jinking from side to side to avoid the bullets which they expected to follow them. Only once did I find myself suddenly face to face with a Wild Boar which stood its ground. It was a large sow with a new litter of nine horizontally striped piglets. One look at the lowered head and tiny, burning eyes was sufficient to make me back cautiously away as quickly as the boggy ground permitted. The old boars, acutely alert from frequent affrays with hunters, were very difficult to approach, though I managed to see one or two of the great hairy beasts, grizzled and grey with age and with dramatically long, curved tusks. Boars shot on the Coto have reached weights of up to 200 lb. and are certainly not creatures to be trifled with on foot. When wounded and cornered in dense vegetation they can be very dangerous and they kill many hunting dogs.

The Lynx of the Coto Doñana is of course of the heavily spotted southern race. Unlike the typical European race which inhabits forests, the Spanish Lynx is a beast of the open bushy scrub of the south, though a few pairs may still remain on the slopes of the Pyrenees. It is a handsome creature, occasionally reaching a weight of more than 50 lb. Unfortunately, like so many of the larger carnivorous animals of Europe, it suffers constant persecution, to which its accessible habitat makes it particularly vulnerable. Probably it is already on the road to eventual extinction. Fortunately, however, those on the Coto Doñana enjoy a secure refuge and today the population is thought to be between 150 and 200. Only fifteen to twenty may be shot each year and the stock is thus being well maintained. Since the virtual disappearance of the Wolf from the Spanish plains, man is the only enemy of the Lynx and even he has little real cause to kill it, as, unlike the Wild Cat and Fox, it does not raid chicken-houses.

On the Coto the chief food of the Lynx is the Rabbit and, to a lesser degree, the Red-legged Partridge and the fawns of the Red and Fallow Deer. Hares, goats and lambs are occasionally killed, but these are seldom numerous on the Coto. An excellent study of the general biology of the Spanish Lynx was published in 1957 by Tono Valverde. In this he described the relationship of the animal to its enemies and prey. I reproduce on the next page an adaptation of one of his interesting diagrams by permission of the author and of Prof. François Bourlière, editor of *La Terre et La Vie*, in which the original paper appeared.

Lynxes are creatures of remarkably conservative habits and they have their favourite hunting routes, which enable the *guardas* of the Coto to discover their lairs. We found their pug-marks in many of the sandy regions. The lairs used for breeding may be earth burrows, hollow trees,

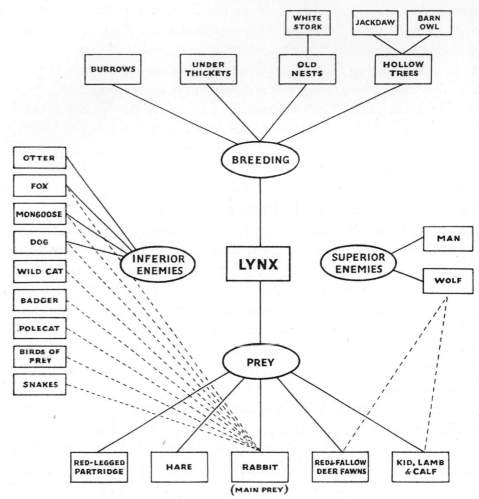

The relationship of the Lynx to its enemies and prey

After J. A. Valverde

or snug cavities under impenetrable briars or thorn bushes. Sometimes old nests of White Storks are used, for the Lynx is, of course, completely at home in trees. The rutting season is in January and the *guardas* told us

XXXII *Above:* The Sand Skink, which has almost lost the use of its puny legs. *Centre:* The blind and legless Burrowing Lizard. *Below:* The Mediterranean Chameleon

b. Don Mauricio González with a Lynx; some of these
animals have to be shot when they kill too many fawns

XXXIII a. The author and George Shannon at the remains of

of the wild catawauling by which the animals seek their mates. The litter varies from one to four, the average number being two. The young do not leave the lair until about four months old, when they begin to be taken on educational hunting parties. Tono Valverde has shown that the Lynx is a fastidious feeder. It eats only the lower part of the neck and shoulders of fawns, only the head and fore-quarters of the Rabbit and only the head, breast, legs and wings of the Red-legged Partridge. The remains are always scrupulously buried, but apparently are never dis-interred thereafter, though this firmly established habit is obviously a relic of a time when the Lynx would return to eat carrion. These shallow caches are frequently to be found on the Coto; I discovered one which contained the posterior half of a Rabbit and another with only the feet, back, wing-feathers and tail of a Red-legged Partridge. In both cases the entrails also had been left. One day I found on the edge of the desert the site of the kill of a Lynx, though the tracks were mostly obliterated. I could see where the powerful hind feet had been thrust deeply into the sand for the spring forward from behind the half-buried crown of a Stone Pine. Six feet beyond, amid confused tracks, were a few feathers and spots of blood. Antonio Chico told us he was standing one evening in the doorway of his little house near the Lucio Dulce when he saw a Red-legged Partridge rise from his patch of cabbages. As it did so, a Lynx sprang 6 ft. into the air and caught it between its fore-paws. The prey is never eaten where it is killed, but is first carried or dragged a con-siderable distance. One of the *guardas* saw a fawn dragged 150 yards before the Lynx began its epicurean meal. When young are being fed in the lair there is a sharp increase in attacks on fawns. A few years ago one pair of Lynxes was known to have killed twenty-five fawns before their lair was found and the kittens destroyed. Though there are plenty of deer on the Coto such losses obviously have to be kept in check. When the losses become too numerous, the *guardas* set spring-traps in the hunting trails; these are lightly covered with sand and once the human scent has evaporated they are usually effective. The heavy iron jaws of the traps are cruelly armed with sharp teeth, which hold the animal by the leg until

H

it can be put out of its misery. On one such occasion Tono Valverde discovered a Lynx trapped only by two toes. The animal was roaring with pain and rage and was quite unapproachable. However, Tono refused to let the *guardas* shoot it. Instead, he asked Don Mauricio to attract the animal's attention from the front with his handkerchief, while he crawled up behind and grabbed its hind legs. He then contrived to place his ruck-sack over its head, declaring that, once its head was covered, it would be quite harmless. This proved correct and he was able to pick it up and carry it back to the *Palacio*. Here he set it on the dining table and proceeded to dress its wounded foot, to the astonishment of the admiring *guardas*. No bones had been broken and the Lynx, a magnificent specimen, remained completely tranquil. The moment its head was uncovered, however, it instantly became a veritable whirlwind of spitting, lashing fury. It was shut up for the night in one of the bedrooms and in the morning was found dead—presumably from shock, for its injury had been trivial. The incident was typical of Tono's complete self-confidence and disregard for danger when dealing with animals.

Apart from probably apocryphal accounts, no evidence has been produced that the Lynx will attack humans, though wounded and apparently dead ones have been known to inflict terrible wounds when incautiously picked up. However, a Lynx will not hesitate to attack and kill a hunting dog and, when cornered by a pack, it is treated with all the caution its raking claws merit.

The Otters on the Coto are not competitors for the food of the Lynx and therefore seldom come into conflict with them, though there is a record of one having been killed in an encounter. All the other carnivorous animals—Fox, Badger, Wild Cat, Polecat, Genet, Mongoose, etc. —most of which seek much the same sources of food as the Lynx, are frequently attacked, though probably not deliberately hunted. None is likely to emerge victorious. There is no record of attacks on Wild Boar and it is very doubtful that a Lynx could kill one of these well-armed monsters, though small piglets are taken when opportunity permits. The Rabbit is, of course, the mainstay of a wide variety of beasts on the Coto, ranging from the smaller carnivora to eagles; this competition with the Lynx is, however, usually indirect. Barn Owls and Jackdaws are direct competitors for breeding sites in hollow trees, but there can be no question about the outcome of any conflicts which may arise.

Wherever Rabbits abound in Spain, Wild Cats are likely to be found also. There are certainly some on the Coto Doñana, but their stealthy nocturnal movements rarely advertise their presence. They breed in old rabbit burrows and hollow trees. Attempts to domesticate their kittens have invariably been unsuccessful, for this is one of the most malignantly ferocious of all animals. An adult male shot recently weighed nearly 11 lb. and had brindled greyish fur, striped with black and shading to ochreous on the flanks. The maximum weight attained on the Coto appears to be 15 lb., but in the *sierras* 17 lb. has been recorded.

Although Hares are not very numerous on the Coto we saw a few on each expedition. Two incidents are worth recording. One day I surprised a Hare crouched in its form far out on a bare mud-flat. I sat motionless on my horse, watching it for about five minutes. The animal then began, with the utmost slowness, to crawl towards a patch of thistles, cautiously lifting one foot at a time, like a cat stalking a mouse. My horse tossed its head and the Hare was off like a flash. On another occasion Pepe pointed to a Hare which also was hiding in its form and he almost succeeded in catching it by hand. His dog then dashed after it. The locality was again a barren one, with no cover. Recognizing that it would have no chance of escaping the dog if it ran in the open, the Hare at once bounded straight to our group of horses, doubling swiftly between their legs, closely followed by the dog. The horses immediately panicked and in the confusion the Hare made a clean get-away.

Until a few years ago the most famous and astonishing animals of the Coto Doñana were the wild Camels, which provided visitors with a sight unlikely to be forgotten. They were extremely wild and difficult to approach and had the added distinction of living, not in the desert region as one would expect, but in the *marismas*. Some writers have referred to the Camels of the Coto as relics of the Moorish invasion. This is not so. About eighty Camels were brought from the Canary Islands to Cádiz in 1829, on the instructions of the Marqués de Villa Franca, for use as draught and pack animals. They created such panic among the horses (which always detest Camels) that they could not be taken into the neighbouring towns of Jerez, Arcos, or Chichlana without causing accidents. They had an equally embarrassing lack of success pulling the plough. Finally they were turned loose on the Coto, where they soon settled down and gradually returned to a completely feral existence, finding unlimited food and seclusion in the open *marismas*, where they even bred quite successfully. Abel Chapman's first report of them in *The Ibis* of January 1884 (by which time the herd numbered sixty) was greeted with incredulity. Wild Camels in Europe—and aquatic at that! It was preposterous! Chapman had already suffered ridicule when he gave the first eye-witness account of the manner in which the Flamingoes of the *marismas* disposed of their long legs when sitting on their nests, and he was justifiably furious. Fortunately Lord Lilford came to his rescue and stated that he had learned of the existence of the Camels as early as 1856. Chapman's later-published descriptions of seeing Camels running across the *marismas* at high speed in clouds of spray, and browsing knee-deep in water, make fascinating reading. He tried repeatedly to approach them, but found this quite impossible, even with the aid of a stalking horse. However, in 1893 the Comte de Paris and a party of *guardas* actually succeeded in running down an old bull and lassoing it. By then the herd had been reduced to about forty and poachers continually harried the remainder, selling their meat as venison to the surrounding towns. By 1950 only five beasts remained and these were eventually stolen, by being driven into a compound to the north of the Coto. The owners of the Coto immediately took legal proceedings to obtain their return, but such is the pace of the law in Spain that as this book goes to press, some eight years later, the outcome has yet to be decided. It is a sad ending to a fascinating story.

I should perhaps include in this chapter a reference to the semi-wild cattle which roam the Coto in their thousands. We were firmly told at

XXXIV   *a.* Building the pylon of Eucalyptus poles at the Kite's
nest in 1956; the nest can be seen on the right

b. Lord Alanbrooke descending the tubular metal pylon erected
for photographing the Spanish Imperial Eagle in 1957

XXXV *a*. Kites with their young, showing the very long tail of the adult. *b*. The nest of the Black Kites was decorated with a profusion of unsavoury rubbish, including part of a peasant's shirt, which can be seen on the right

the time of our first visit in 1952 that we had nothing to fear from the bulls, as these were not *toros bravos*, but mere beef cattle which were 'useless fighters'. The famous fighting stock of Andalucía, from which they were descended and of which we saw many fine specimens behind stout fences elsewhere, were certainly best avoided. None of these now roamed the Coto, though a few years ago they did so and were often very dangerous. Nevertheless, none of us could be quite confident that the enormous bulls which accompanied the herds fully accepted their social relegation and we gave them a wide berth. It was noticeable that the cattle usually ignored us once we were mounted, but that bulls and the cows with small calves were inclined to react aggressively to solitary pedestrians, particularly if we accidentally separated them from the herd. I remember walking alone one evening from Martinazo to the *Palacio* and finding in my path a colossal bull which was moaning quietly to itself and gouging up great lumps of earth with its horns. The assurances I had been given about the harmless nature of the animals entirely failed to convince me that I might walk nonchalantly forward. I debated briefly, 'The *guardas* know and *I* know that this is not a dangerous fighting bull—but does the bull know?' Not being certain of the answer, I made an arduous half-mile detour. Eric Hosking and Sir Julian and Lady Huxley had similarly uncomfortable experiences with the bulls of the Coto, while Lord and Lady Alanbrooke were actually treed by one for a while in 1957.

One of the most dramatic events witnessed during our 1957 expedition took place one evening when, unfortunately, the light was already too poor for photography. A strange bull, of gargantuan proportions, came to challenge the monarch of a herd near the *Palacio* for possession of the harem. Both were splendid beasts, with tremendous shoulders and wickedly curved horns. For half an hour these monsters threatened each other at a distance of 100 yards, bellowing loudly and throwing back clouds of sand with their fore-legs. At the conclusion of this phase both had dug themselves pits, which we afterwards measured at 8 ft. in length by $2\frac{1}{2}$ ft. deep. The bull in possession then walked slowly forward, until it stood shoulder to shoulder with the challenger. With infinitely slow motions they then circled, occasionally scooping up clouds of sand. Finally, and without warning, they clashed head-on, with a sound like the slamming of a heavy door. In spite of its smaller size, the defender succeeded in pushing the challenger backwards for 50 yards before the latter broke free and ran. As in all conflicts of this nature with other animals, possession and mutual awareness of possession were nine points of the law, for by sheer weight alone the challenger should have been able to gain the victory. It was a tragedy that we were unable to record this exciting incident photographically.

The small mammals of the Coto have not yet been investigated in any detail and it is probable that our list (*see* Appendix 2) may be incomplete. The micro-rodents certainly require more study and the fact that we identified ten species of shrews, voles, mice and rats and four bats is a fair indication that there is no shortage of material.

The Coto is exceptionally rich in reptiles and amphibians. During the 1957 expedition we identified five species of snakes, eight lizards or lizard-like creatures, three frogs, two toads, a newt, a salamander, two tortoises and a terrapin. Tono Valverde seemed always to know exactly where to find each species and was for ever jumping off his mule or from the tractor to capture specimens for the photographers. Those he wished to examine at leisure he put casually in various capacious packets or collecting bags and in the evenings used to spill out quite a menagerie on the table. One day he inadvertently put a frog into a bag which already contained a snake; when the bag was opened later the frog was missing and the snake had a comfortable bulge in its middle.

The commonest reptile is the Water Snake *Natrix maura*, a relative of our Grass Snake. In spite of its rather Adder-like markings it is not poisonous. It was found in and out of the shallow water all along the edges of the *marismas* and fresh-water lagoons. Our study of the Short-toed Eagle showed this snake to be its favourite prey. It seldom exceeds 3 ft. in length. The largest species on the Coto is the quite formidable Montpellier Snake *Malpolon monspessulana*, which is common in the coastal region and particularly around the pine woods, to which it is attracted by the abundance of Dormice, Pine Voles and Rats which feed on the pine seeds. In turn it is preyed on there by the Mongoose, which has been chiefly attracted by the hosts of Rabbits feeding in the grassy clearings. One sees here a good example of the interdependence of the various inhabitants of a natural community. The Montpellier Snake is moderately poisonous, but, as its poison fangs are set very far back, it is unlikely to be able to use them in striking at a human unless it succeeds in getting, for example, a finger well inside its mouth. It is a dimorphic species, some being greenish-brown and others almost black. Abel Chapman referred to 'the Black Snake' in a way which suggested that he mistakenly regarded the melanistic form as a distinct species. He shot one which measured 6 ft. 2 in. and we heard that a length of 7 ft. had been recorded on the Coto. These monsters have voracious appetites and Chapman found two full-grown Rabbits, both freshly killed, in one specimen he examined.

The Ladder Snake *Elaphe scalaris* is also numerous. This is a harmless species, growing to about the size of the Water Snake. It is easily identified by the characteristic ladder-like bars between the two parallel dark lines on its back. The one really poisonous species on the Coto is Lataste's Viper *Vipera latasti*, a sinister-looking beast with a small horn on its nose. Although we seldom saw Vipers they are common in the scrub and around the dune areas and they are not infrequently willing to cross wide expanses of bare sand (*see* Plate LVIII). Eric Hosking was the only member who had an opportunity to examine one of these snakes closely, having shared his hide with one for a considerable period. He was too engrossed with the birds he was photographing to try to get rid of it, though he warned me to tread carefully when I came later to relieve him. The fifth snake of the region is the harmless little Southern Bordeaux Snake *Coronella girondica*. To find the 'Bordeaux' and 'Montpellier' snakes in the wilds of the extreme south of Spain is to demonstrate how stupid is the habit of naming creatures after restricted localities, instead of giving them descriptive names. As will be seen in Appendix 3, three further species of snakes occur elsewhere in Andalucía.

Among the lizards of the Coto, pride of place unquestionably goes to the spectacular Ocellated, or Eyed, Lizard *Lacerta lepida*. In appearance this heavily built creature recalls an iguana rather than the slender little lizards to which we in the northern parts of Europe are accustomed. It has a heavy body and a broad head with powerful jaws which can inflict a not inconsiderable bite if it is handled incautiously. Although it has no poison glands its saliva is liable to make the wound septic. We saw no specimens exceeding two feet in length, but the species is known to grow to three feet. I watched a very large one hunting in the scrub one day and was impressed by its magnificent colouring. Its body was pale green, closely covered with tiny golden dots; down its flanks were three rows of large blue spots. Its throat was pale blue, with vivid yellow markings around its massive jaws. Eric Hosking, Pepe and Tony Miller succeeded in cornering one in the open sand and found it amazingly defiant, preferring to stand and threaten with wide-open jaws rather than run away (*see* Plate XXXI). The Ocellated Lizard feeds on other lizards, birds and small mammals. It is an inveterate egg-thief. Chapman killed one which contained not only the full clutch of a Bee-eater but the parent bird also, which had been killed in its nest-hole. On another occasion he saw one pull a squealing half-grown Rabbit by the leg from its burrow.

The slender, long-tailed Algerian Sand Lizard *Psammodramus algirus* is the most numerous species on the Coto. Every sandy trail through the scrub is criss-crossed by its dainty tracks. It is easily recognized by the conspicuous white lines down its flanks. The more heavily built Spine-foot Lizard *Acanthodactylus erythrurus* is plentiful in open areas. Its body is whitish, finely mottled with dark brown. The Wall Lizard *Lacerta bocagei liolepis* and the attractive little Moorish Gecko *Tarentola mauritanica* occur around the *Palacio*, huts and watch-towers.

There are two extremely interesting lizards which provide good examples of the intermediate evolutionary stage between the true lizards and slow-worms. One is the Sand Skink *Chalcides bedriagai* (or perhaps *C. striatus*, we were not certain which species was involved). This is a rather helpless, stubby-tailed little creature with very small, almost rudimentary legs, which seem so puny in relation to the weight of the

XXXVI *a*. The sombrely-coloured Black Kite poses at its nest in a Stone Pine. *b*. The more graceful Kite with its two sturdy young in the crown of a Cork Oak

body as to be almost useless. It is found chiefly in the scrub areas, where it must be particularly vulnerable to the numerous predators. The other, the Grey Burrowing Lizard *Blanus cinereus*, is a completely legless lizard. It grows to a length of 4 to 5 in. and as it lives just beneath the surface of the ground and under litter it has lost the use of its eyes. Its shiny, tightly scaled body seemed almost incapable of forward movement when we placed it on a polished table, merely wriggling helplessly from side to side. On the rough ground, however, it made fair progress where its scales could obtain some purchase.

The slow-moving and always amusing green Mediterranean Chameleon was found clambering among the Halimium bushes, looking as usual like a character from a Walt Disney cartoon film.

Great numbers of frogs and toads were found along the edges of the *marismas* and around the lakes and fresh-water lagoons. The commonest species is the beautifully marked Southern Mud Frog *Pelobates cultripes*, which represents one of the most important items in the diet of many birds and reptiles. When George Shannon was photographing the Spotless Starling at its nest he was startled to see what appeared to be one of these stout frogs being carried in the bill of one of the parents, who gave it to the nearly fledged nestlings. This is probably the first time that a starling has been seen to take so large a prey. We found the miniature emerald-green tree-frog, known as the Canary Islands Hyla *Hyla arborea meriodionalis*, in many of the reed-beds and the big Marsh Frog *Rana ridibundus* also. The familiar Natterjack Toad *Bufo calamita* is known to occur on the Coto, though we did not see it.

Five races of the Spotted Salamander have been described in the Iberian peninsula. The one on the Coto is *Salamandra salamandra hispanica*. We saw one of these being given to young Kites in 1956. The only newt we identified was the Pleurodele Newt *Pleurodeles waltl*.

Our ecological examination of the Coto showed clearly that each of the different habitats—the dunes, the lakes, the pine woods, etc.— attracted its own distinctive community of animals. Some species accepted only closely restricted combinations of several factors such as vegetation, terrain and humidity, whereas others, more catholic in their taste, tolerated quite wide variations and occurred in several habitats. The following is a very rough *précis* of Tono Valverde's study of the animal communities, conducted as part of the general ecological survey which Max Nicholson and he carried out (*see* Chapter 18).

1. In the coastal dunes and slacks, with scattered pine woods and sparse undergrowth in the moister hollows, the following occurred: Lataste's Viper, Montpellier Snake, Spine-foot and Sand Lizards, Greek Tortoise, Garden Dormouse, Pine Vole, Brown Rat, Mongoose and Red Deer.

2. In the dry scrub areas, with Halimium, Genista, Bramble, Bracken, Tree Heath and scattered Cork Oaks, thorn thickets and occasional moist hollows: Lataste's Viper, Montpellier, Ladder and Southern Bordeaux Snakes; Ocellated, Sand, Spine-foot, Wall and Grey Burrowing Lizards and Sand Skink, Greek Tortoise, Hedgehog, Polecat, Genet, Mongoose, Fox, Wild Cat, Lynx, Wild Boar, Garden Dormouse, Brown Rat, Hare, Rabbit and various small mice and bats.

3. Along the edges of the *marismas* and fresh-water lagoons and lakes, with reeds, rushes, Marram Grass, patches of open meadow, etc.: Water Snake, Terrapin, Pond Tortoise, Hyla, Marsh and Mud Frogs, Natterjack Toad, Pleurodele Newt, Garden Dormouse, Water Vole, various mice, Rabbit, Fallow Deer and Wild Boar.

4. Around buildings and ruins: Wall Lizard, Gecko, Garden Dormouse, Brown and Mediterranean Rats and various small mice and bats.

The redoubtable Wild Boar

9

THE BIRDS OF PREY

NO FEWER than twenty-seven of Europe's thirty-eight species of birds of prey have been seen on or very close to the Coto Doñana. At least thirteen of them have bred there and eleven probably still do so regularly. It is an amazing total and possibly without equal in any other area of similar size on the Continent.

Three vultures, the Griffon, the Black and the Egyptian, are constant visitors. The Bearded Vulture has occurred at least once. Five eagles may still be seen, the Imperial, the Short-toed, the Booted, the Golden and, at longer intervals, the Bonelli's; the first three breed there, the other two being visitors from the *sierras*. The Marsh and Montagu's Harriers are residents and the Hen Harrier occurs in winter. Buzzards and Hobbys breed there in small numbers. Honey Buzzards pass through regularly on migration. Peregrines and Kestrels are residents and Lesser Kestrels occasional visitors from across the river. Kites and Black Kites nest in large numbers and the Black-winged Kite has been recorded as a rare vagrant. Goshawks, Merlins, Eleanora's Falcons, Sparrow Hawks and Ospreys have all been seen and the last two have bred there in the past. Even vagrant White-tailed, Tawny and Spotted Eagles are said to have been shot in the neighbourhood, though the records are now too old to be verified or accepted.

The Rough-legged Buzzard, which breeds in northern Scandinavia, had never been recorded in the far south-west of Europe until Tony Miller saw three migrating northward over Gibraltar with a party of

Buzzards on 7 May 1957. He was alone at the time and, although his report was carefully documented, it seemed so improbable that our scrupulously careful recorders were disinclined to accept it. However, on 15 October of the same year I clearly identified another of these birds flying south along the Costas de Málaga, near Marbella, towards Gibraltar. Like Tony I was well acquainted with the species in its breeding grounds and the bird was flying so low as to be quite unmistakable. Both records are now accepted, though they are not, of course, included in the totals quoted above for the Coto. Nevertheless, the Coto is only about eighty miles by direct flight from Gibraltar and right in the path of migrants following the west coast of Spain; the birds seen by Tony would almost certainly have flown over it.

One of the objectives of our 1956 expedition was to photograph the Kite and the Black Kite. Both have a particular interest for British ornithologists. In Shakespeare's day kites made a major contribution to the public health of our cities by scavenging refuse in the streets. They were at that time well protected and became so confident that they would take crusts from the hands of children on London Bridge. The poet described London as 'a city of crows and kites'. Today their place in the Cockney's affection has been taken by the London pigeons. Whether the species concerned was the Kite or the Black Kite, or both, will never be known; but as the Black Kite is the familiar scavenger seen today in many primitive countries, I suspect that this was the bird, though we certainly also had the other species in country districts. Now, alas, after centuries of senseless persecution at the hands of gamekeepers, farmers and egg-collectors, only about twenty-five pairs of our Kites survive, in a closely guarded hill area in Wales. Our town birds were probably lost by a combination of this persecution and the advent of enclosed sewers.

There was no difficulty in finding either species on the Coto, indeed the skies were seldom clear of them. We examined several nests of the Kite, at heights varying from 20 to 40 ft. above ground. On 7 May choice was finally made of a nest in a tall Cork Oak containing two downy chicks aged about three weeks. True to the tradition mentioned

XXXVII *a*. Black Kite on a Red Deer carcase; these birds feed on carrion more frequently than the Kites. *b*. Ravens usually waited until the vultures had completed their feasts before visiting carcases, but this one was hungry and came early

XXXVIII *a*. Tony Miller supervises the dragging of the poles across the scrub for the pylon at the Short-toed Eagle's nest, while Tono Valverde rides by with a load of cross-members. *b*. James Ferguson-Lees, *left*, and Pepe building the pylon

by Shakespeare's Autolycus, the nest also contained an unsavoury collection of rags, paper, bones, cow-dung and other refuse. It was in a position which permitted a hide to be erected where the best photographic advantage could be obtained from the sun, with the minimum interference from intervening foliage. Like all good bird-photographers Eric Hosking, who directed all our photographic operations, has a rooted objection to 'gardening', i.e. to cutting away the cover around nests. His very proper insistence on this point presented a tricky problem, which was finally overcome by the removal of only two small branches and a few twigs.

Looking back on the erection of the tree-top hide at the Kite's nest, I can only thank Providence that we succeeded without breaking any bones. On this expedition we had come quite unprepared to construct a 35-ft. scaffold and were dependent on whatever materials we could find on the Coto. The following year we were better equipped. Fortunately the resourceful Antonio Chico discovered some slender Eucalyptus poles at the *Palacio* and a few old sherry cases which could be made into a platform. These were cached in the undergrowth near the tree. We decided that the pylon should be built by easy stages, so that the birds should get used to it gradually. Work was to be restricted to a maximum of forty-five minutes each morning. We had brought climbing irons, but they were of little assistance as the pylon had to be constructed against the slender outer branches, none of which would support a grown man. Happily salvation appeared in the person of the incomparable Pepe, whose bare-footed agility and complete disregard for the laws of gravity and equilibrium quickly earned him the nickname 'El Mono' (the monkey). While the heavyweight *ingleses* held the poles upright, Pepe swarmed up them and leaped lightly out among the swaying branches, cutting here and deftly tying there, until the first 'storey' was firmly anchored. The erection of the second 'storey' was much more difficult, as it depended on lashing the roughly mortised and nailed ends of the poles one on top of the other. The tops of the lower poles were only $2\frac{1}{2}$ in. across, while the bases of the upper ones were about $4\frac{1}{2}$ in. Perhaps it was as well that none of the enthusiastic builders possessed the technical knowledge to calculate the stresses involved as the flexible cross-members were lashed to the uprights with ropes of dubious vintage.

On the fifth day the platform was hauled into place and the green canvas hide secured to it. From the lens opening the nest could now be examined from a distance of only 11 ft. This was the final test of the birds. Would they accept this sudden bulky addition to the tree? As we rode away that morning there were many anxious backward glances at the two finely angled silhouettes of the Kites, wheeling high above the tree.

Next morning, as we drew near, the female was seen to leave the nest and a quick inspection showed that the nestlings were happily digesting a recent meal. All was well. Quickly Eric Hosking swarmed up the creaking scaffold and pulled up his precious cameras behind him on a nylon rope. The hide was firmly pinned up and he was left to his lonely vigil.

Nine hours later we relieved him. Hearing us approach, he stuck his head out of the hide. One look at his face, crimson with the heat but beaming with triumph, told us that he had succeeded. As he slithered down the pylon he kept up an incoherent running commentary. 'Simply terrific . . . couldn't have been better . . . an absolute peach of a bird . . . both parents at the nest!' We clustered round, eager for details. He had taken a long series of pictures, which we were later to recognize as some of the finest of his career as Britain's leading bird photographer (*see* Plates XXXV & XXXVI). The Kites had behaved with exemplary confidence and Eric had been so engrossed that he had forgotten to eat his lunch, but had sustained himself for nine gruelling hours on a small flask of tea. As a strict teetotaller he had to put up with a good deal of ragging for refusing to drink the ambrosial sherries which our host, Don Mauricio, so generously donated to the expedition from his *bodegas* in the heart of Spain's sherry-producing region.

On the following days George Shannon and Roger Peterson each spent long periods in the Kite hide and took hundreds of feet of colour film of the parents and young. On George's second spell a high wind sprang up and he was in hourly fear of the pylon collapsing. Through holes in the floor he could see the mortised joints yawning alarmingly and the lashings becoming progressively more slack. Nevertheless he stuck to his post until satisfied that he had completed his documentation. We gave orders that the *guardas* should dismantle the pylon next day, as it was unsafe for further use; but a year later we found it still standing, albeit somewhat drunkenly, and the Kites apparently again nesting in the tree.

During the period of observation a number of interesting notes were made. The female seldom permitted the male to stay longer than a few moments at the nest. Usually she snatched the food he brought before he had time to fold his wings, though occasionally he managed to feed the young himself. In thirty-four daylight hours during which notes were made in the hide, the female brought food to the nest eleven times and the male nine times. It was not always possible to identify what was brought, but Rabbits predominated. Other food included snakes, Red-legged Partridge (probably surprised on the nest), a large lizard and a Garden Dormouse. It appeared that the Kites fed on carrion much less frequently than the Black Kite, which we studied later.

The Kite is not only a complete master of the art of soaring and gliding, but is a most beautiful sight to watch in flight. To see one rise from the ground is to gain an impression of weak and laboured flight, but once it has climbed to a sufficient height, it spreads its 'sails' and begins to soar in wide circles. The flexible primary wing-feathers open like sensitive fingers, seeking to gain maximum advantage from the eddying thermal currents. The graceful, deeply forked tail swings loosely from side to side, now closed, now open to its fullest extent, twisting at times un-believably at right angles to the horizontal plane. Like the vultures, the Kite likes to sit on a favourite perch in the early mornings, waiting for the sun to heat the ground and bring forth the rising thermals. As its food is largely slow-moving prey and occasional carrion it has little need for speed in level flight. Nevertheless it succeeds in catching a variety of less agile mammals and birds, as well as snakes, lizards, fish, toads and frogs. Dragonflies are often caught in flight. Earth-worms are obviously considered a delicacy. With such large numbers of semi-wild cattle living on the Coto there is no shortage of carrion, though this is much less important to the Kite than to the Black Kite. Myxomatosis struck the region in 1955, but failed to wipe out the Rabbits, which evidently bred immunity to the disease and are today as numerous as ever, to the great benefit of Kites and other raptors.

Seen at close quarters, the Kite is a richly coloured bird of graceful proportions. Its pale head is strongly streaked with black, the eye being large, with an amber iris, and the hooked bill is delicately shaped by comparison with an eagle's. The body is a rich reddish brown, the feathers of the upper parts being boldly edged with buff. The long, angular wings have black primaries, with large and conspicuous whitish patches beneath. The very long swallow-tail is a rich, pale chestnut.

Several pairs of Black Kites were nesting near by and they shared a common hunting ground with the Kites we photographed, though they guarded their nest-trees actively. Eric Hosking saw 'his' Kites playing tag in the sky with three Black Kites, twirling around among them and giving vent to long, quavering cries. As a final *pièce de résistance* the pair of Kites flew face to face, seized each other's talons and, to the accompaniment of a series of high-pitched mewing notes, deliberately fell several hundred feet before parting. In 1957 we saw a Kite chasing a Black Kite which was carrying food; after a magnificent display of aerobatics the Kite succeeded in taking hold of the food, but the Black Kite refused to let go and the two birds fell to the ground with their talons interlocked on the prey. The Black Kite was then seen to rise and carry off the trophy.

Having succeeded with the Kite, our next task was to photograph the Black Kite. There were nests galore, as they outnumbered the Kites by about twenty to one. We selected a nest so conveniently low in a Cork Oak that the sitting bird could just be photographed from ground level. The female was sitting on a single egg. After the rather glamorous Kites, we found her a trifle uninteresting and her sombre dark brown plumage rather drab. Even in flight the Black Kite compares unfavourably, being less agile. This impression is heightened by its much shorter, almost

128

XXXIX The most striking feature of the Short-
toed Eagle was its piercing, orange-yellow eyes

square-ended tail. However, our spells in the hide were enlivened by the constant stream of feathered visitors to the Black Kites' nest-tree. Lord Alanbrooke filmed some of them merely by swinging his camera in the hide—a Bee-eater, a Melodious Warbler, a Turtle Dove, a Little Egret and, of course, the ubiquitous Jackdaws.

The documentation obtained of the Black Kite in 1956 was by no means complete, as the egg did not hatch before we left. In 1957 we therefore tried again. An attractively sited nest in the fork of a Stone Pine near the Corral de la Cita was chosen and a 20-ft. pylon was gradually erected. The nest was only 18 ft. from the ground and was decorated with a long, tattered piece of a white shirt dangling down one side and a piece of rope down the other. In the nest were the remains of a Redshank, a snake, a kid, a Brown Rat, a Rabbit, two empty cigarette packets, some lumps of dry cow-dung, two eggs and a sturdy chick. Nests of this species are always more unsavoury than those of the Kite. The parents quickly accepted the pylon, with its hide perched on top, and behaved beautifully. Eric Hosking obtained many excellent pictures of them (*see* Plates XXXV & XXXVI) and Lord Alanbrooke took some fine cinematograph sequences, in one of which the male is shown bringing to its mate the offering of a piece of tattered grey cloth. As with the Kite, the male was rarely permitted to feed the nestling himself.

At the time of our 1956 expedition about six pairs of Spanish Imperial Eagles were present on the Coto—an astonishing number considering the rarity of the species. On 7 May we visited four eyries, none of which yet contained eggs, though three appeared to have had fresh sticks and greenery recently added. Two at heights of 35 and 40 ft. were in Cork Oaks, and two in the crowns of Stone Pines, at 18 and 35 ft. respectively. Probably the exceptionally cold February weather and snow, which ruined the Olive and citrus crops of Andalucía that year, had affected the eagles. Another nest, 45 ft. up in a Cork Oak at Bellota Gorda, contained a small chick on 8 May. It was examined at a distance of about 15 ft. and the young bird appeared to be either dead or perhaps shamming, for the parents were still attending the nest. A further nest, from which young had recently flown, was found by Don Mauricio a month after our party had left the Coto. We observed Imperial Eagles in various parts of the study area on numerous occasions. Most, if not all of them, appeared to be fully adult, with the striking pure white 'shoulder' patches on the very dark wings, which is the distinguishing mark of the Spanish race of this splendid species. I had an unusual opportunity to observe an adult at very close quarters in 1952, when one sailed over me at about 25 ft. while I was lying on my back in the scrub, taking a siesta. It flew to a tree near by and called repeatedly, in a harsh, rasping voice, 'owk, owk, owk'. The species is much more vocal than most eagles.

An account of our experience in finally photographing the Spanish Imperial Eagle at the nest in 1957 forms the subject of another chapter.

Two or three pairs of Booted Eagles breed regularly on the Coto, though we failed to find a nest. The species is dimorphic and we saw adults in both light and dark plumage phases on a number of occasions, weaving among the trees in powerful but graceful flight. Those in the light phase had white 'wing-linings' and very pale bodies, while the dark phase birds were uniformly dark brown below, except for their pale, un-barred tails. Seen overhead in bright sunlight, the clear pinkish-brown of the rather long, square-cut tail is very distinctive. The heavily feathered legs, from which the bird gets its name, can be seen only at close quarters. The Booted Eagle is locally diminishing in numbers; Tono Valverde has suggested that this is the result of the gradual disappearance from the Coto of its favourite nest-tree, the White Poplar *Populus alba*.

The other medium-size eagle typical of the Coto is the Short-toed Eagle, or, as many prefer to call it, the Serpent Eagle, which is perhaps a more appropriate name. Many of Europe's eagle species have at one time or another been seen in Great Britain, but this bird is an exception. Its breeding range extends through southern Europe and parts of Africa to northern India and the delta of the Ganges. The present western range lies south of a line running roughly from the Loire to Alsace. The European population is partly migratory, some birds wintering as far south as Nigeria, Egypt and Abyssinia. It is nowhere numerous.

Although it feeds almost exclusively on snakes, lizards and frogs and can therefore by no stretch of imagination be called harmful to man, it suffers the usual senseless persecution which is inevitably reserved for the large birds of prey. Already it has disappeared from Germany; it is rare in Switzerland and diminishing year by year in France. Laying but a single egg each year, its chances of long survival in Europe appear slender. Oh for effective international conservation measures!

The Short-toed Eagle is in many ways paradoxical, both in its appearance and in its highly specialized feeding habits. It has the majestic, powerful flight of an eagle, yet hovers like a Buzzard. Its very large orange eyes and broad face are distinctly owl-like, but its small bill and shaggy 'trousers' recall the typical harrier; its curiously small grey feet, which give rise to its name, are unlike those of any other bird of prey. In flight it is chiefly remarkable for its very large wings and rather large, distinctively projecting head. Seen flying overhead it looks chiefly white, with narrow black tips to the flight feathers. One then notices the three dark bars on the tail, a light sprinkling of spots on the lower surfaces of the wings and body and a brown flush on the upper breast and throat. The plumage is however very variable and some birds are almost completely white below. The upper parts are a delicate shade of grey-brown. The female, contrary to the rule with most true eagles, is not noticeably larger than the male; it is browner than its mate, which has a pale grey head.

We were determined in 1957 to find and photograph the Short-toed Eagle and so were delighted when the *guardas* informed us on our arrival that they had already located an occupied eyrie. This proved to be in a particularly remote part of the Coto, not far from the Charco del Toro. To reach it we had to make a long, cross-country ride through the scrub, followed by half a mile of hard going across the dunes. The site was superb, the eyrie being only 25 ft. from the ground in the crown of a Stone Pine, on the sheltered side of the main ridge of the dunes, with the sea half a mile beyond. Other Stone Pines and Juniper bushes were scattered around the site in a most picturesque setting. James Ferguson–Lees put on his climbing irons and inspected the nest. Our faces fell when he announced that it contained an apparently fairly fresh egg. We dared not disturb the bird by erecting a pylon before the egg hatched and we had only four weeks left. Would it hatch in time? Reluctantly we agreed to wait and to make a weekly inspection. We had, however, fortunately misjudged the freshness of the egg, for less than two weeks later it hatched. Work began immediately on the assembly and transportation of the materials for building a pylon. All the prefabricated elements of Eric Hosking's tubular scaffolding were already in use at a Spanish Imperial Eagle's nest and at the nest of an Azure-winged Magpie. We were therefore obliged to make new scaffolding out of Eucalyptus poles, which, as we had learnt to our cost in 1956, meant a great deal of hard and difficult work. But worse still was the problem of transporting four heavy 28-ft. poles, with twenty-four cross-beams and a platform, across the final half mile of very loose and steeply undulating sand, in a temperature of well over ninety degrees in the shade (a reading taken in a hide). And there was no shade. Our heavy tractor managed the first part of the cross-country journey successfully, but the last lap was a nightmare. Some of the poles were dragged over the sand by mules (for the horses refused to tackle such an unusual operation), while the remainder were man-handled by a stalwart team consisting of Tony, James and Pepe, who worked like slaves (*see* Plate XXXVIII). Three days were fully occupied with the erection of the pylon, under Eric's direction. The final edifice, if more than a trifle wobbly, was at least well secured by guy-ropes at the four corners. But Pepe, who usually disregarded all caution, pulled a long face and said, '*Muy malo.*' I fully confirmed his opinion when I climbed up. It made the rickety scaffolding built the previous year at the Kite's nest seem as solid as the Rock of Gibraltar!

Our usual practice was to let Eric Hosking take the first pictures of any rare bird. However, on this occasion, as I had to return to England the following day, my colleagues voted that I should have the honour of being the first man to photograph the Short-toed Eagle. I was delighted by the gesture and settled myself in the hide, prepared for a thrilling day.

XL *a*. The young Short-toed Eagle about to be fed on a small Water Snake. *b*. The grey-headed male *left* has just regurgitated the rear part of an Ocellated Lizard, which its mate is about to give to the nestling. Note male's more heavily barred tail

XLI *a.* The first Griffon Vulture approaches the carcase, balancing itself on partly open wings. *b.* The horrid feast begins; in 27 minutes only bare bones were left. On the left is a Black Vulture and a very much smaller Egyptian Vulture

It was ten o'clock in the morning, the light was excellent and a breeze from the sea kept the temperature in the hide at a quite comfortable level of about 80°F. Through the peep-hole I could see the eaglet, now about twelve days old and looking like a white woolly toy, only seventeen feet from me. Its crop looked flat and empty, which meant that it was likely to be given a meal quite soon. It lay sprawled comfortably on its bed of pine needles, fast asleep. I lit my pipe quietly and prepared for the great moment when the parent would alight on the nest, carrying, I hoped, a good big snake.

An hour passed, two hours, three hours. I was quite prepared to wait. But I was becoming increasingly anxious about the wind, which seemed to be rising steadily. The pylon was rocking badly and I had already re-set my shutter to its maximum speed to compensate for the movement. Another hour passed and the wind rose higher. There was still no sign of the eagle. I now had to keep my eyes really close to the peep-hole, otherwise the rocking of the pylon carried it out of sight of the nest. The whole fabric of the pylon began to groan and creak in the most alarming fashion. No self-respecting bird could possibly return to its nest with this racket going on, I told myself. But at that moment I caught sight of a long-winged form wheeling over a tree 100 yards beyond the nest. It was the eagle at last. Finger on trigger I waited tensely. On my left I heard the eagle cry, a rather weak 'ke, ke, ke'. This is not the usual cry of the Short-toed Eagle, but probably an anxiety note. The normal cry, heard later by Eric Hosking, bears some resemblance to that of a courting Tawny Owl—an emphatic '*mew-ock!*'

Another hour passed uneventfully. The nestling was getting hungry and stood up unsteadily, scanning the surroundings. It was a comical little creature, with remarkably projecting eye-sockets, which gave it the appearance of wearing old-fashioned motoring goggles. The adult eagle has very large, frowning eyes, but no trace of such curious projections. Suddenly the eaglet looked intent, with head thrust forward, and then began moving it from side to side, in the way some birds do in order to obtain a parallax 'fix', or focus, on an object. 'At last, the female is approaching,' I thought, and my finger itched to press the shutter-release. Alas, the wretched nestling flopped down and went to sleep again.

By six o'clock the wind was blowing half a gale and the pylon seemed in great danger of collapsing. Every guy-rope was twanging, every joint groaning loudly and the canvas hide billowing like a ship's sail, although I had pinned down all the ventilators. Photography was now out of the question, as my heavy tripod would no longer stand still on the rocking platform. Through the cracks in the boards I could see the tree tops beneath me bending right over in the wind. I reflected that if the worst happened they might at least break my fall. Sadly I packed my equipment and waited for Pepe to come and relieve me. When, shortly afterwards, he did so, I was thankful to return to *terra firma*. My last day on the Coto that year had been exciting enough, though not in the way I had hoped.

A week later Eric Hosking tried his luck with the Short-toed Eagles. He, too, had to contend with a rather high wind off the sea, but he took the precaution of adding four more guy-ropes to the top of the pylon, which steadied it somewhat. The birds by then had grown accustomed to the hide and he obtained some excellent pictures and films. Later John Parrinder also had a spell in the hide and succeeded in making sound recordings of the voices of the nestling and its parents.

After a wait of only three-quarters of an hour, Eric heard one of the eagles calling overhead. An hour later the male alighted on the nest-tree. From its bill dangled a few inches of the tail of a snake. Descending confidently to the nest, it put one foot on the snake and pulled out the headless body, which was about 2 ft. long. It was one of the numerous local species, the Water Snake *Natrix maura*. The eagle stood on the still writhing form and began tearing off small pieces, which it presented delicately to the hungry nestling. The meal lasted for nearly half an hour and was just concluding when the female arrived at the nest, bearing a sprig of fresh pine needles, which she added to the lining. These additions to the nest continue to be made until the young eagle is fledged and serve a very useful function in keeping it in a sanitary condition. The hen then settled to brood the chick, which scrambled gratefully under her feathers to escape the blazing sun.

Seen at close quarters from the hide the large eyes of the adult eagles were startling in their extraordinary brilliance. They are a vivid, luminescent orange-yellow and quite unlike those of any other eagle. The plumage of both birds was unusually handsome, the bold horizontal markings on the flanks being particularly striking and darker than normal.

On the second visit of the male the nestling immediately seized the dangling tail of the snake which protruded from its bill and began pulling. The parent again assisted the process of disgorgement with its foot, but the nestling did not release its hold during the tug-of-war which resulted. With quick backward motions of its head it began swallowing the 2-ft. snake, tail first. It was, however, soon obliged to regurgitate and to begin again, head first. In an astonishingly short space of time it engulfed the whole snake, although its own total length at that age was scarcely 10 in. But an even more amazing performance was filmed on another occasion. The male carried to the nest a snake nearly 3 ft. in length and 1½ in. thick at its widest part. This was received by the female, who began tearing off tiny pieces for the nestling; but the latter soon got hold of the snake and began swallowing it. After gobbling the first 8 in. at a tremendous rate, it began choking and had to disgorge. It quickly began again, gulping at a steady rate of once every three to four seconds. By the time it reached the thickest part of the snake its tiny bill was stretched open to its fullest extent and the weight of the carcase made it fall over on its side. Hanging on grimly, it righted itself and continued its gargantuan meal, but pausing now from time to time in complete exhaustion. At the end of thirty-seven minutes the tip of the snake's tail finally disappeared and the nestling collapsed, its downy crop distended to half the size of its tiny body. Three and a half hours later it cheerfully ate another snake! The rapidity of the digestive processes of the young eagle was obviously phenomenal.

Several different species of snakes were given to the nestling.

Although not immune from the bite of poisonous species, the Short-toed Eagle does not hesitate to kill and eat the big Montpellier Snake, or the much more dangerous Lataste's Viper. The hind-quarters of a large Ocellated Lizard were also brought to the nest (*see* Plate XL).

While hunting, the Short-toed Eagle flies slowly, occasionally gliding briefly on level wings, at fairly low altitude, hovering from time to time, or hanging motionless, head-on to the wind. When a snake is spotted, the eagle thrusts its head downward, half closes its great wings and drops like a thunderbolt, seizing the wriggling prey on its outstretched talons and bearing it quickly aloft. Like the smaller Buzzard it often sits motionless for long periods, either on a tree or on the ground. In this respect one might call it a rather sluggish bird, but anyone who has seen it hunting will agree that it fully justifies its classification as an eagle.

Golden Eagles, which probably do not breed within forty miles of the Coto, were seen several times in April and May on all three expeditions. The Bonelli's Eagle, another mountain species, is a rare visitor, though Abel Chapman succeeded in shooting one or two wanderers on the Coto outside the breeding season. A few Buzzards nest there regularly and we found several nests in Cork Oak trees. Marsh Harriers were seen every day in considerable numbers; they breed in many areas around and in the *marismas*, as do a few Montagu's Harriers. Hobbys were observed in May each year and in 1957 they were plentiful. They are late breeders. Abel Chapman said they never bred on the Coto. On our final year we were convinced that those we saw were not merely birds of passage but were paired and settling to nest there. Peregrines were not numerous, but on all three expeditions a pair was found breeding on the 52-ft. Torre Carbonero watch-tower; we saw the young on the wing in 1957. Kestrels nest regularly and are very common, but the graceful little Lesser Kestrel finds no suitable nesting sites and is only a visitor to the Coto, though breeding in large numbers on buildings and cliffs on the other side of the river. Migratory parties of Honey Buzzards, in light and dark phases, cross the Coto in spring and autumn every year. We saw a mixed party of five on 9 May 1956, and I have several times observed large numbers passing over the Strait of Gibraltar and following the western coast of Spain in the direction of the Coto.

It is perhaps not inappropriate to mention in this chapter the owls which occur on the Coto. We found both Barn Owls and Little Owls fairly common and breeding, but heard the mournful piping of a Scops Owl only in 1957. Short-eared Owls occur in considerable numbers on migration and in winter. Abel Chapman claimed that Eagle Owls had occasionally been shot or heard in the region; they are of course resident in other parts of Andalucía, though usually in the mountains. Tawny and Long-eared Owls are rare in southern Spain and have not been recorded on the Coto, but we saw one of the former during our explorations in the *sierras*. Finally, an eighth species of owl has occurred as a vagrant in Andalucía, the Algerian Marsh Owl *Asio capensis*. This resembles a dark Short-eared Owl, with black instead of yellow eyes and almost un-feathered blackish feet.

Short-toed Eagle chick's gargantuan meal

10

THE VULTURES OF ANDALUCÍA

I AM not one who subscribes to the popular judgment that vultures are horrible creatures. There is a fascination in watching these great birds at close quarters and their mastery of soaring flight is always a source of wonderment. Their service to mankind throughout those parts of the world which they occupy is of inestimable value. Indeed without these greedy scavengers, to which nothing comes amiss, a great part of the over-populated tropics and semi-tropics might well be almost uninhabitable. They provide the only *corps sanitaire* in many regions where human survival is precariously balanced against disease and pestilence.

Three species of vultures occur regularly on the Coto Doñana—the Griffon and the much smaller Egyptian, which are numerous, and the Black, of which only small numbers are likely to be seen. The rare Bearded Vulture has been recorded only once. The first two nest in inaccessible mountain caves and fissures of rock at medium to high altitudes; the third is chiefly a tree-nesting species, breeding in tall pines in the central mountains of Spain. Both the Griffon and the Egyptian nest in the *sierras* within thirty miles of the Coto; on different occasions we saw flocks of as many as seventy of each species, while the maximum number of Black Vultures observed at any one time was only five. The largest mixed flock seen was eighty birds; but in April 1953, during a visit to the Coto, John Wightman and Peter Westall saw a flock consisting of 150 Griffons, 20 Egyptians and 8 Blacks around the carcase of a cow.

I might here mention an interesting story, recounted by Tono

Valverde. Apparently he was told by some Arabs in Morocco that anyone who made a wish while sitting in an Egyptian Vulture's eyrie could be sure it would come true. This so fired the imagination of James Ferguson-Lees that when he succeeded in climbing to one of these nests in the mountains explored by our advance party, he promptly squatted down on it and wished fervently to add the Great Bustard and Glossy Ibis to his list of birds seen in Spain! Before the expedition ended he had seen both.

We were particularly anxious to obtain some photographs of vultures. In 1952 Roger Peterson and I had tried unsuccessfully, first with an old mule carcase and then with the fresh carcase of a deer. There were plenty of vultures about, but not one would come down. In 1956 we determined to try again with a more putrid carcase and by good fortune came across a dead cow not far from Martinazo which was unquestionably 'ripe'— indeed, it could be approached only with a handkerchief held to the nose. Roger was jubilant and insisted that it should be moved to a more photogenic site, where he could photograph waiting vultures perched on the picturesque branches of an old dead tree. None but the hardy James Fisher was prepared to support this ambitious enterprise. With great determination they went off to get a tractor and ropes. The decomposed body was dragged through the bracken to the chosen site, two well-concealed hides were erected and Roger and George Shannon were left to await the vultures. Throughout the remainder of the long, hot day they sat there, the perspiration trickling down their backs. Not a bird came near. The following day George and Jerry Jamieson tried again and succeeded in obtaining one fleeting portrait of an Egyptian Vulture on the carcase. The sequence was, however, afterwards found to be too brief to be included in our film. The attempt was abandoned. Roger sadly declared that there must be a jinx on his photographing vultures, as he had been similarly unsuccessful with attempts in America.

A few days later Roger and I were on the mud-flats at El Puntal, photographing Black-winged Stilts and Pratincoles. Late in the afternoon, just as I was on the point of deciding that I would move my hide, Antonio Chico came riding up with the news that he had found a party of *buitres* (vultures) feeding on a carcase. As a confirmed optimist I was immediately interested. Jumping on my mule, I rode off to tell Roger. I found him sitting happily in his hide with muddy water up to his ankles, photographing Stilts. He shook his head dubiously, but agreed to go with me. We rode with Antonio about half a mile across the marsh, to where two or three vultures were circling. There, on the edge of a shallow lagoon, we found, alas, nothing but the skeleton of a Red Deer, with part of the hide still adhering. It could not have looked less promising. Moreover there was not a vestige of cover for a hide.

'Not a chance,' declared Roger. 'You'll never get the birds to accept a hide here and the carcase is already picked clean.'

'I'm going to try, nevertheless,' I said. Roger good-naturedly helped me to put up a hide on the far side of the lagoon, about 50 ft. from the bait, and lent me his big 300 mm. telephoto lens. There was a slight breeze which I judged might cause some vibration, so I decided to try first with my lighter 200 mm. lens.

To my astonishment, no sooner had Roger and Antonio splashed away over the horizon than an Egyptian Vulture alighted and began tearing at the carcase. I began shooting. Shortly afterwards it was joined by another and finally by two more. Chortling with triumph, I took a series of colour pictures and then changed over to my black and white camera and the big lens for some close-ups. As I expected, as soon as I poked the new lens out of the slit in the hide the birds flew. Cursing under my breath I sat back and lit my pipe, preparing for a long and almost certainly unrewarded wait. After writing up my notes on the Egyptian Vultures, I glanced casually out of the peep-hole. I gasped at what I saw. Beautifully grouped around the deer stood an Egyptian, a Griffon and, marvel of marvels, a magnificent Black Vulture! Without bothering to check the focus, I fired the shutter and obtained what everyone afterwards agreed was one of the most important and certainly the luckiest of the pictures taken on the expedition. It was the first time that the three species had ever been photographed together and also the first close-up picture taken of the Black Vulture.

XLII *a*. A fine picture of a Griffon Vulture soaring, showing the 9-ft. wing-span and short tail. *b*. Unlike the herons, the White Stork extends its long neck in flight

XLIII *a*. A characteristic picture of Eric Hosking, who directed all the photographic work during the 1956 and 1957 expeditions. *b*. The author with a stuffed Eagle Owl, used for studying the 'mobbing' reactions of certain birds

Two more Griffons then alighted, though too far back to be in focus. Before I could adjust the camera all the big vultures hopped clumsily a few paces away. I got in two more exposures before they retired farther and then flew, leaving only one Griffon, which sat somnolently for half an hour before departing. Evidently all the birds were well fed and I was extraordinarily lucky in getting them at the carcase at all.

When Roger and Antonio came to pick me up an hour or so later I was beaming. I shall never forget Roger's disappointment that he had not elected to try, but he was generous about my success.

I had been interested to find the bare, wrinkled skin of the Egyptian Vulture's face such a brilliant yellow. The plumage of the body is a brownish white, the under-parts and wings white, with contrasting black flight feathers. Seen in the sky from below, the Egyptian has a bold black and white pattern similar to that of the White Stork. The tail is, however, rather long, wedge-shaped and tapering to a point. The bird is, of course, only about half the size of its big cousins the Griffon and the Black Vultures. Nevertheless it has tremendous muscular strength. I was astonished to see one of those I photographed brace its foot against the carcase of the deer and tear the skull right off the neck and carry it quite easily in its narrow bill a distance of some 10 ft. The Egyptian Vulture is somewhat handicapped, however, by the rather delicate proportions of its bill and it usually waits for the larger species to tear open the hides of the bigger animals.

The Griffon and Black Vultures are of similar size, with wing-spans of up to 9 ft. The Black is usually slightly the larger and much the heavier of the two and has been known to reach a span of just under 10 ft. In flight both have round-tipped wings and very short tails, but the Griffon's tail is almost straight-edged, whereas the Black's is clearly rounded and therefore looks longer. This may however be an unreliable diagnostic feature, as the tails are often worn down by feeding and roosting on rocky ground. Both species, when adult, have a characteristic 'ruffle' around the base of the neck, but the Griffon's appears white (in reality a dirty buff) whereas the Black Vulture is uniformly black. The extremely heavy, hooked bills are similar in shape, but that of the Black Vulture is considerably deeper in vertical plane than the Griffon's. Seen on the ground the plumage of both species is shaggy and loose, but those I photographed were in excellent condition and impeccably clean; when the breeze ruffled the Griffon's feathers I could see the pure white down beneath them.

My success with the vultures that year was followed in 1957 by a much more important documentation. We had not yet succeeded in obtaining a cinema record of a vulture feast and we placed this high on our list of tasks for our final expedition. Because of the drought, carcases of cows, horses, deer and boar were extremely numerous that year and vultures were having the time of their lives. Soon after we arrived, Antonio Chico told us that one of his bulls was dying. We asked that when the poor beast expired its carcase should be taken to a suitable spot near the *Palacio*. A couple of days later, at three o'clock in the afternoon, the skinned carcase was put out and two hides were erected. No vultures were in sight and we judged that most of them were by that time of day heading back across the river to the *sierras* for the night. We decided to man the hides early next morning. At six o'clock the same evening we happened to be riding back past the carcase. As we approached we saw tell-tale specks circling over the spot. Closer inspection revealed more than seventy vultures, most of which were sitting in some trees near by. Hastening forward we found a clean-picked skeleton, with the heavy leg bones scattered in a radius of 30 yards. Not a trace of flesh remained and the ground was trampled like a muddy football pitch (*see* Plate XXXIII). We had failed again.

Chagrined, we decided to try once more. A few days later we were working in the Puntal region and saw forty vultures circling over a newly dead foal. This time we would make no mistakes. A hide was put up and I went straight in. I stayed until dusk in a sweltering temperature. Not a bird came near. Early next morning Lord Alanbrooke and Eric Hosking tried, reinforcing the bait with the carcase of a deer. Again nothing came. In desperation Eric decided to try once more the following day. As the

Americans say, this time he 'hit the jack-pot'. First came a Raven and two Black Kites, then an Egyptian, then twenty-seven Griffons and finally two Black Vultures. In a wild *mêlée*, snarling and growling and clambering on each other's backs, they demolished the carcase completely, down to the polished bones, in exactly twenty-seven minutes. Later the smaller scavengers reappeared, a Raven, two Magpies, a Kite and four Black Kites. Eric meanwhile had been feverishly working alternately with his black and white and colour cameras and a cinema camera, recording every incident of the feast. His success was complete and beyond our wildest dreams. We had at long last beaten the vultures.

The fourth and rarest of the vultures of Andalucía is the famous and very solitary Bearded Vulture, or Lammergeier, as it is often called. Like the Egyptian, it has pointed wings; the tail is also wedge-shaped, but proportionately much longer. The head is rather small and narrow and the characteristic stiff, black 'moustaches' are difficult to see in flight though very visible when the bird is perched. There is nevertheless no mistaking the dark flight silhouette, with the narrow, distinctively angled wings and long tail. This magnificent bird is unfortunately becoming very scarce, but it may still be seen in the high *sierras* of south and central Spain and occasionally in the Pyrenees. It has not been recorded over the Coto Doñana for many years, though Chapman saw one there on the carcase of a horse in 1883. We did not see any during our expeditions; I saw one later, however, in the Sierra Nevada, where several pairs still nest among the inaccessible peaks. They are fortunately still holding their own in the Atlas Mountains on the other side of the Mediterranean, and my wife and I had a splendid view of one at short range when we were having a picnic lunch at Ouirgani, 4,000 feet above sea level in the Moroccan Atlas, in 1952. The Spanish call the bird *Quebrantahuesos* (the bone-breaker) because of its interesting habit of carrying the leg bones of carcases high into the air and then dropping them on the rocks in order to smash them and eat the marrow. A good eye-witness account of this habit appears in Willoughby Verner's *My Life among the Wild Birds of Spain*, published in 1909.

Provided that one has the wisdom to select a position up-wind, watching vultures feeding is an interesting if rather ghoulish experience. I was able to observe such incidents several times in India and the Middle East during the war. All vultures exhibit great caution in making the first approach to a fresh carcase, but excessive greed once the banquet has begun. The first bird to arrive circles cautiously overhead, gradually dropping lower and then examining the carcase closely from ground level or from adjacent perches on rocks or trees. Others arrive and begin waddling slowly around. Eventually one pecks tentatively at some soft part such as the eyes or belly and jumps back to see if there is any response. Once satisfied that the animal is dead, the birds begin the horrible orgy with feverish haste. Before long the carcase is smothered under a heaving, flapping, growling, hissing mob of vultures, which quickly become fouled with the viscera as they plunge their heads and shoulders inside the gaping holes torn in the body. In an incredibly short space of time nothing but the skeleton remains. Gorged with food, the vultures stagger away a few paces, temporarily incapable of flight. Other scavengers, such as the smaller vultures, carrion-eating eagles, kites, jackals and dogs, are then able to take their share.

I have several times seen the astonishing manner in which vultures discover and assemble over a carcase. The sky has been completely clear of birds when, apparently from nowhere, the first dark speck has materialized overhead. Within moments of its gradual descent other vultures have appeared from various directions and begun gliding down in converging flight. Undoubtedly vultures have magnificent long-range vision and watch each other and the smaller scavengers as they patrol the skies; a downward movement is the signal awaited and this is instantly passed on for miles around, as one after another follows suit.

Tono Valverde told me an interesting story about his efforts to trap a live vulture. The idea was an ambitious one, for all these birds are exceptionally wary. Outside many villages in Spain, as in the Far East, there is usually a long-established spot to which the carcases of animals are taken for disposal by vultures. They and the starving village dogs

XLIV A magnificent portrait of the rare Spanish Imperial Eagle and its nestling, aged 4 weeks

know these localities well and feed there regularly. Tono set a trap at one and confidently expected to catch his vulture. Instead, all he caught was twenty-three dogs!

There is a large and long-established roost of Griffon Vultures on the beetling cliff at Arcos, where the great birds can be observed at close quarters. It was here in 1956 that Roger Peterson finally triumphed over his jinx by obtaining a superb film of the Griffons soaring on the thermal currents rising against the cliff. In order to follow their movements he used a cinema camera mounted on a gun-stock. Each detail of the birds appears in true colours in his film. The slow-motion sequences of the gliding and soaring flight show every sensitive movement of the great wings as they quiver and flex to the changing eddies and currents. The final dramatic scene shows a Griffon dropping long legs and volplaning vertically downwards to enter its cave.

Nobody has yet ascertained the maximum altitude to which vultures will soar. During the war I saw several at heights of up to 15,000 ft. above sea level when I was in aircraft flying in Africa and they have been seen at much greater altitudes in the Himalayas. One day on the Coto I was lying on my back in the scrub, scanning the sky with 8 × 40 binoculars adjusted to full range, when I picked out a group of circling vultures at such an altitude that they appeared only as tiny straight lines, their heads and tails being invisible. I speculated that at such a height the birds could probably see across the Strait of Gibraltar to the African coast spread out far below them.

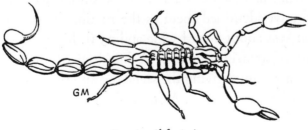

Scorpion (life-size)

11

A DAY AT MARTINAZO

THE slight breeze had dropped and the day dawned with a clear blue sky and a low haze over the *marismas*. The huge influx of Spotted and Pied Flycatchers, Turtle Doves, Golden Orioles, Rollers, various warblers and other immigrants had passed on and the trees which yesterday had been alive with birds were strangely silent. The temperature mounted steadily to about eighty-five degrees in the shade by noon. In the evening, as we rode slowly back from Algaida to the *Palacio*, the midges began to emerge from the boggy patches among the scrub. The air was soon full of them. Fortunately they appeared not to bite humans. I discovered later that they were not our familiar and much-disliked blood-sucking *Culicoides*, but one of the several hundred species which feed on plant juices.

The following morning, as we set out for a day at the heronries, an astonishing sight awaited us. As far as the eye could see, column after column of what at first looked like black smoke rose from the scrub. Approaching, we identified them as the mating swarms of the midges. Each column was about a yard wide and 25 ft. high and emitted a high-pitched hum of amazing volume. A hundred or more columns were visible at the same time, giving the scene the appearance of a vast bivouac area, with smoking camp fires. As we rode through the swarms our faces and clothing were blackened with myriads of the insects, which crawled inside our open shirts and into our eyes and ears.

During that day a new phenomenon occurred—the emergence from

146

the *marismas* of countless small red dragonflies (*Sympetrum fonscolombei* and *Crocethemis erythraea*), which at once began to prey on the midges. In this task they were in competition with many shrikes, flycatchers and the larger warblers, which were again passing through on migration. By next day the midges had completed their swarming ceremonies and were no longer visible. The dragonflies, however, had been discovered by the Bee-eaters, which circled in graceful, swooping flight to catch these tasty morsels. Every few minutes the birds alighted momentarily on the ground to beat their victims on stones, or to regurgitate gleaming black pellets of their chitinous elytron. Profiting from a light breeze, many thousands of small spiders were also on the move. To embark on their mysterious migrations they first spun long, wind-borne loops of gossamer; when the strands were long enough to support their infinitesimal weight one end was cut adrift. Embracing the other, the spiders relinquished their hold on *terra firma* and were carried aloft on the fragile rafts created from their own substance. Soon every tree was wearing intercepted streamers, glittering down-wind. Invisible strands met high in mid-air and coalesced to form sticky, shining ribbons, which attached themselves to the wings of the circling Bee-eaters, until the birds appeared to be leaving glinting trails behind them, like the vapour-trails of high-altitude aircraft.

I spent most of that day in a hide, watching a pair of handsome Great Grey Shrikes feeding their six nestlings in a small Ilex Oak. When I emerged I found that my clothing was crawling with the small, noisome ticks *Hyalomma excavatum*, which infested the surrounding Halimium bushes. We never succeeded in spending any time in the scrub regions without finding that ticks had secured a foothold on us. Once they reached the skin they quickly set about their blood-sucking business and were then extremely difficult and unpleasant to remove. After toiling back to the Martinazo hut with my cameras and other paraphernalia, I stripped and sat in the shade to disinfest my clothes. An inquisitive Bee-eater and a Woodchat Shrike soon came to perch on a leafless tree near by to watch me. They preened their feathers and the shrike sang prettily at intervals, in-troducing snatches of a Sardinian Warbler's alarm notes for good measure.

Suddenly there was a hissing rush of wings and I looked up just in time to see a splendid Short-toed Eagle stooping at the Bee-eater. The attack failed by inches, as the two smaller birds dived in terror from their perches. The eagle's talons struck the bare branch, leaving it quivering under the impact. With a powerful flap of its long, white-lined wings the bird rose again and flew in leisurely fashion to a distant tree. It was an intensely exciting incident, but I suspected that the attack was merely in play, as the Short-toed Eagle normally feeds only on snakes, lizards and frogs.

Lighting my pipe, I leaned back against the warm mud wall of the hut, pulled my hat down over my eyes to shield them from the glare and looked out over the shimmering *marismas*. A large herd of semi-wild horses was galloping through the water in a cloud of spray, about half a mile away, and the sound came clearly to me like distant thunder. Above them galloped in space another herd, by the trick of a mirage. Forty miles beyond hung the lilac frieze of the Sierra de San Cristobal, jagged against the arching blue dome of the cloudless sky. When the horses came to a standstill there was no sound but the wavering cry of a Kite, far out over the marsh, and the thin '*dzeep . . . dzeep*' of an invisible Fan-tailed Warbler. I concentrated on trying to impress the profound sense of space, peace and beauty on my mind, so that I might take it with me, back to the hurly-burly of London, where all is noise and hurry and where even the crocuses in the parks are soiled with grime before they can open to the pallid sun. London seemed like a place on another planet. Here such things as the inescapable compulsion of the telephone bell were as unthinkable as any other of our tokens of servitude to modern civiliza-tion. Sixty years ago Abel Chapman had sat where I was sitting, to contemplate the mysterious beauty of the *marismas*. Nothing had changed. Time stood still on the Coto Doñana. I realized that after only three weeks in such an atmosphere I had already lost the habit of glancing at my wrist-watch. The sun had become my timepiece. James Fisher had recently remarked thoughtfully that riding on the Coto was like riding back into the Middle Ages. One half expected to see Felipe IV and his hunting

XLV *a*. The Spanish Imperial Eagle and its nestling at the age of 5½ weeks. *b*. The eagle brings a full-grown Rabbit to the eyrie; the young bird is now about two months old and its pale brown feathers are growing rapidly

XLVI *a.* A well-camouflaged Stone Curlew incubating its eggs and panting in the hot sunshine. *b.* The Savi's Warbler looked rather like a large Reed Warbler, but its song recalled the brief churring of a Grasshopper Warbler

companions come galloping past, *lanza* in hand in pursuit of a Wild Boar, as they did here in 1624.

I knew that by raising my binoculars in any direction I should see birds, living as they had done for countless generations, secure from man in the midst of never-failing sources of food and shelter. Natural enemies, of course, abounded, for all nature subsists on predation; yet the balance between the weak and the strong remained delicately counterpoised, the more vulnerable creatures maintaining their positions by their ability to hide, or to flee, or by their greater fecundity. In the space of only a few hours had I not just witnessed four progressive stages of predation—the eagle which attacked the Bee-eater, which preyed on the dragonfly, which preyed on the midge, which sucked the life-blood of the bog plants? It was like the nursery rhyme of the house that Jack built. Even the lordly Imperial Eagle was not immune, for its numbers were held in check by man and by occasional four-footed and feathered egg-thieves and by the competition of other large raptors for its food and *Lebensraum*. Only modern man contrived to upset the ecological balance of nature; man the destroyer, who now killed not for survival but for pleasure; man the despoiler, who razed forests and polluted rivers; man with his mixture of ignorance and sentimentality, which led him to 'introduce' animals and plants into finely balanced communities where, as often as not, they set off a long and tragic chain of unforeseen reactions.

I was roused from my reverie by an unusual movement on my left. On an area of open ground a Magpie was indulging in strange antics, dancing back and forth around a patch of dwarf Palmetto palm. Its actions were clearly aggressive, yet fearful. Round and round the tuft of vegetation it danced, its tail almost vertical and its wings half open. Growing bolder, it pounced forward, stabbing quickly with its bill. The next moment it plucked a writhing, 2-ft. snake into the open. Again it circled, jumping back and forth, stabbing from left and right. Finally, by jumping high in the air, it succeeded in landing on its victim, which it hammered with repeated, violent blows. The battle was soon over. After eating most of its kill, the Magpie picked up the

149

remainder and flew away with it to its nest in a Bramble patch, where, as I knew, it had six hungry nestlings. It was the first and only time I have seen a Magpie kill a snake, though it was a common enough sight to see Short-toed Eagles doing so. Snakes were very numerous on the Coto. Birds nesting on the ground, or in holes, suffered greatly from them. Even the aggressive and self-reliant Jackdaws could not escape them; we were warned not to put our hands into their nest-holes in trees or Rabbit burrows in case the occupant turned out to be a Lataste's Viper. One day Roger Peterson was filming a Stone Curlew returning to its nest and obtained a delightful sequence when it discovered a small snake coiled among its eggs. The bird stopped dead and gazed at it, with that extraordinarily statuesque intensity which no other species can quite equal. Then, infinitely slowly, it reached forward and suddenly flicked it out of the nest. When the little snake had wriggled away the Stone Curlew straddled the eggs and, keeping its head absolutely motionless at a fixed point, very slowly lowered its body, with its neck growing longer and longer in between. When its body was comfortably settled on the eggs it telescoped its neck slowly downward and merged, as motionless as a stone, into the litter of dead twigs around it.

That evening, when we were unloading the mules outside the *Palacio*, I tried in my halting Spanish to describe the snake incident to one of the *guardas*. He listened politely, but when I mentioned the word '*serpiente*' (snake) he dropped his eyes and looked embarrassed.

'*Quiza un lagarto*' (perhaps a lizard), he said, stirring the dust with his boot. No, I assured him, it was a snake, 'so big', and I held out my hands. He shook his head and walked away. I was a trifle puzzled, but thought no more about it. Later, however, Don Mauricio told me that the local peasants are deeply superstitious about snakes and that even to mention the word is considered bad luck. If discussion is unavoidable they are always referred to as lizards, in order to fend off misfortune. Nevertheless, the cast skin of a snake is believed by the peasants to be an excellent cure for headaches if worn tucked inside the lining of one's *sombrero*. Should the Andaluz be bitten by a poisonous snake he has a remedy ready in his pocket—a section cut from the base of a Red Deer's horn. He applies a tourniquet above the wound while he boils the piece of horn in milk or oil. This is then applied to the wound and sucks out the poison. I was assured that the process was efficacious, but John Raines, our medical officer, maintained firmly that he would prefer to rely on the anti-toxins with which we were equipped.

We noticed one day that the son of one of the *carboneros* was wearing a sprig of Halimium behind each ear. Recalling the habit of the Papuan infantry, who wore orchids behind their ears while fighting in the Solomon Islands campaign in the last war, I assumed that this was done for the decorative effect of the yellow flowers. Don Mauricio told me, however, that this was another example of the local pharmacology—a cure for stomach-ache!

These charming incidents only strengthened my impression of the Coto as a mediaeval oasis in a highly industrialized western Europe.

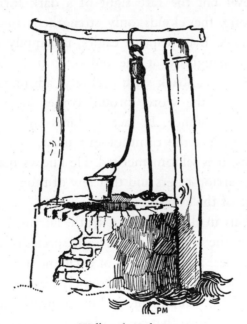

Well at the Palacio

12

THE SPANISH IMPERIAL EAGLE

EVEN to the layman eagles have an irresistible appeal. As children we are brought up to think of them as fierce, noble creatures. Statesmen and soldiers instinctively choose their likeness to symbolize majesty and courage. A host of exciting, if usually highly improbable, folklore surrounds them. Those who actually see eagles in a free state are very few; but the rare sight of a dark form wheeling high and remote among the clouds only strengthens one's impression of mysterious aloofness. Even captive eagles, unhappily immobile behind strong bars, glare haughtily at the onlooker from beneath frowning brows; whether we gaze back with curiosity, admiration, pity, or even with a thrill of fear, the word 'proud' comes inevitably to mind in considering their appearance. In fact no birds enjoy a more generally splendid reputation. Yet the ornithologist must, alas, admit that, with notable exceptions, it is seldom merited. He knows that some eagles are sluggish, ignoble carrion-eaters and that few of them can match the self-confident courage of the average Robin.

Having said this in the interest of truth, let me hasten to add that, though I have seen the majority of the eagle species of the world in their natural state, I still feel a strong thrill of excitement every time I set eyes on one. Eagles are solitary birds and extremely difficult to observe closely. Nowhere are they really abundant. In Europe nearly all the species now occur in such small numbers that conservationists are increasingly exercised about their survival. Some of the larger kinds, such as the White-tailed, the Spotted, the Tawny and the Imperial, retain only a precarious foot-hold. In Great Britain we have long since shamelessly exterminated the great White-tailed or Sea Eagle, which used to nest around our coasts. Thanks to enlightened measures of protection and a bounty system to reward gamekeepers, the remnants of our Golden Eagle population, perhaps 180 pairs, have been saved in Scotland from a similar fate. Unfortunately, however, bird protection is in its infancy in many countries and few species suffer such universal persecution as the large birds of prey. Only in parts of south-eastern Europe, Russia and the south of Spain can one now be reasonably sure of seeing more than one species of eagle in any one locality. To see four kinds in a single day, as we did on several occasions on the Coto Doñana, is unique in western Europe. There, of course, our chief interest lay with the Spanish Imperial Eagle, which is certainly one of the rarest and most magnificent birds in the whole of Europe.

The Imperial Eagle *Aquila heliaca* has a distribution in small numbers ranging from Greece, Jugoslavia and Asia Minor and parts of north-east Africa, across palaearctic Asia to Japan. It is essentially a bird of the steppes and plains. In build it is large, with sombre, blackish-brown plumage, relieved only by the pale, tawny crown and nape. Fully adult birds have a few white feathers on the scapulars. In the old days the geographically isolated race living in the southern Iberian peninsula and Morocco was treated as a distinct species, then called the White-shouldered Eagle *Aquila adalberti*. It is now recognized as a sub-species which has broken away from the eastern population and has therefore been given the scientific trinomial *Aquila heliaca adalberti*. It is, in my opinion, the most handsome of the European eagles. Its plumage is a rich, dark chocolate, with a burnished gloss on the feathers of the back. The most striking features are the snow-white markings on the leading edges of its fore-wings and on either side of its upper back, which are clearly visible even in distant flight. Like the eastern form, the Spanish bird has a very pale sandy crown and nape. Its powerful bill is the colour of bluish horn.

The distribution of the Spanish race is confined to the southern parts of Spain and Portugal and a few localities in Morocco, north of the Atlas range. No accurate estimate can be made of its numbers, but they are certainly very small. As it nests on the plains and lowlands it unfortunately does not benefit from the natural protection enjoyed by species which breed among inaccessible mountains. Its nest is a tremendous edifice, usually all too visibly located in the crown of an isolated tree.

We discovered six pairs of Spanish Imperial Eagles on the Coto Doñana and in 1956 we located most of their eyries. Like most eagles, each pair had an alternative nesting site not far away, which was used from time to time. The great spring frosts of 1956, which were the worst in Spain's recent history, may have contributed to the fact that only two pairs attempted to breed. The single nestling of one pair appeared to be dying when we examined it and we decided not to attempt any photography that year. The other pair succeeded in rearing two flying young. In 1957 a severe drought, which lasted almost without a break throughout the winter and spring, upset the entire ecology of the Coto and its adjacent *marismas*. Nevertheless all six pairs of these eagles attempted to breed. One produced two fine youngsters, only to have them killed by an ignorant peasant trespasser from El Rocío, who doubtless suspected the parents of robbing his chicken-run. Two other pairs, with one and two nestlings respectively, were in locations too inaccessible for us to keep them under observation and we did not learn whether they survived. Two more eyries had fresh materials added to them, but eggs were not laid. The remaining pair, which had a single nestling and an infertile egg, was the one selected for detailed study and photography.

The Spanish Imperial Eagle had never yet been photographed and this task was given top priority among the objectives for our final expedition. Having carefully studied the eyries on the previous visit, we concluded that in order to do the job thoroughly we should be obliged to build a solid pylon of anything up to 40 ft. in height, on which to erect the hide. We therefore shipped to Gibraltar, in advance of our arrival, half a ton of Eric Hosking's now famous tubular metal scaffolding, which he had used so successfully for tree-top work in England. As things eventually turned out, the nest we photographed was at an exceptionally low altitude, in the exposed crown of a Stone Pine, only 24 ft. above ground; but the extra rigidity provided by the scaffolding paid handsome dividends. The site was a very pleasant one, among scattered, flat-topped pines growing in sand, in the region known as the Corral Quemado.

The young eagle was about twenty days old when we arrived. Knowing the penalty for disturbing its parents, we erected the pylon by very easy stages, giving the birds ample time to get used to the strange edifice growing up beside their tree. Each morning we worked for about an hour, at top speed, hoisting the metal tubes into position and securing them by strong clamps. On the sixth day the hide was lashed to the platform and all was ready. Eric Hosking, cautious as ever, wanted to give the birds forty-eight hours' respite, so I asked that nobody should approach within half a mile of the area. Finally, on 12 May, Eric was installed for his first spell of nine and a half hours, in a temperature which by early afternoon soared to 96°F. in the hide.

It was five hours before the eagle returned to the nest, bearing a Rabbit, which she quickly plucked and dismembered for the young bird. Twelve minutes later she departed and was seen no more that day. Eric had succeeded nevertheless in obtaining a fine series of pictures, which amply repaid the hardships of his long wait. During the following two and a half weeks he had six more days in the hide, in order to secure photographs of the development of the young eagle. The parent had by then become confident of the harmless nature of the hide and behaved excellently, remaining at the nest on one occasion for three and a half hours.

George Shannon had the honour of making the first cinematograph film in colour ever taken of the Spanish Imperial Eagle and its young. These were obtained in the course of an eight-hour session on the day following Eric Hosking's first visit. Lord Alanbrooke was the next to use the hide. Although I know of no septuagenarian who looks so deceptively young, or who is more active, I was by no means happy that he should endure the long grilling in the merciless heat of the tree-top hide, much less that he should climb the 30-ft. pylon, with its difficult 3-ft. 'steps'. But he had already filmed the Golden Eagle in Scotland, in circumstances little less arduous, and was indignant at the least suggestion that he should be deprived of this opportunity to make an even more exciting film. I accompanied him to the site and watched him climb with complete confidence up the pylon. When he rode back to the *Palacio* that night he appeared less fatigued than any of us and he was in tremendous form later at dinner. The amazing stamina which sustained him under the frightful burden he shouldered throughout the last war, which was the envy and despair of all who served under him, had very obviously not deserted him.

Having satisfied myself that the basic pictorial documentation had now been secured, I had two enchanting days at the eagle's nest, on 15 and 19 May. On both occasions I was able to obtain some good pictures, but most of my time was occupied in studying the behaviour of the young bird and its parent. The copious notes I made, with those compiled by other members, who passed a combined total of eighty-three hours in the hide, provide a valuable consecutive record of the progressive changes in the domestic routine at the nest and the development of the chick. Like most young creatures, the young eagle passed much of its early days in sleep. The nest was completely without shade until evening and I marvelled that the tiny bundle of life, protected from the fierce sun only by a coat of white down, could survive day after day of pitiless heat. In the hide the temperature stood for hours at over ninety degrees. Stripped to the waist, I found it almost unbearable, but refreshed myself periodically by pouring a little water over my head and shoulders. Like Eric Hosking, I made my mid-day meal on oranges, lest the crackle of the paper in which the inevitable fish *tortillas* were packed should reach the acute ears of the eagle.

As the days passed, the young eagle developed with great rapidity. At the time of my first full day in the hide it was about twenty-eight days old and the first traces of the brown tips of the scapular feathers formed symmetrical patches on its white down. Four days later the scapulars

156

XLVII · The tiny Fan-tailed Warbler, one of the most characteristic birds of the Andalusian lowlands, builds an exquisite nest copiously bound with spider webs

XLVIII *a.* A female Sardinian Warbler at its nest in a Pistachio bush. Both sexes have brilliant red eye-rims

b. A male Sardinian Warbler feeding nestlings. Its extensive black cap and white throat are very conspicuous

were completely feathered and brown speckles had appeared on the back, breast and flanks, while the tips of the emergent feathers on the wings and tail were already an inch long. Two weeks later the nestling was almost as big as its parent. Its body was by then well covered with *café-au-lait* feathers, leaving only its head and thighs in white down. On the primary feathers of its wings were two large white patches. Unlike the nestling Short-toed Eagle (*see* Chapter 9), the young Spanish Imperial looked every inch a baby eagle, from the fiercely curved black tip of its large yellow bill to the powerful claws on its big feet.

The eagle chick was just learning to stand on its grotesquely long legs during my first visit. It did this experimentally several times, flapping its embryo wings and then collapsing quickly on to its behind. On my second visit it was still unsteady on its legs, but was scrambling all over the nest, often standing on the very edge to look over the side, teetering backwards and forwards so alarmingly that I expected any moment to see it fall to the ground. It had now learned to void its excrement clear of the nest, which it did very neatly by climbing to the rim and elevating its rear. The ground beneath the tree thereafter soon became ringed with 'white-wash'. Whereas the nestling had slept for sixty per cent of the eight hours of my first visit, less than thirty-five per cent of the time was now passed in sleep.

The young eagle was a great favourite with all of us because of its consistently comical behaviour. Even while sleeping it continued to maintain this reputation, by sprawling on its side, with one wing and one long leg fully extended and its head as often as not hanging sideways over the edge of the nest. Before it mastered the use of its legs it often used to sit balanced on its thighs, with its big yellow feet held vertically on either side of its head. It looked laughably uncomfortable. On one such occasion it caught sight of its feet, drew back its head in apparent surprise, looked carefully from one to the other and then tried to swallow one of its toes. A few days previously our field party had come across a semi-wild goat giving birth to twin kids, one of which died. The following day a kid, probably this one, was carried by the eagle to its eyrie. One of the leg bones became the favourite toy of the nestling, which played with it for hours, nearly choking itself in repeated efforts to swallow it. Sometimes it actually swallowed one end and sat with the remaining two-thirds protruding grotesquely from its bill, going through agonizing contortions in attempts to engulf the remainder. Neither did it hesitate to try swallowing the bone cross-wise. A large pine cone, which can be seen in Plate XLV, was another unfailing attraction and the chick struggled manfully to detach it.

The arrival of the parent was usually heralded by the alarm cries of a pair of Magpies, which had a nest a few hundred yards distant. The young eagle soon learned to associate the anxious chatter of these birds with the arrival of food and would instantly raise its head, peering intently to the left of the hide, from which direction the adult would approach. When later the young Magpies left the nest and wandered past the eyrie, the young eagle did not connect their conversational notes with the alarm, but merely craned its neck to watch them in the surrounding trees. As soon as the flying eagle was spotted, the nestling scrambled to its feet and began crying in an urgent falsetto, a repeated, thin, wheezy 'see-uk'. On my second visit it introduced an infant version of the adult's deep, barking 'owk . . . owk'. It did this quite by chance during a spell of play and rehearsed it several times with evident satisfaction, looking round jauntily to see whether the performance had attracted attention.

The arrival of the parent with food created an immediate change in the entire appearance and behaviour of the young eagle. In place of the self-confident, aggressive little creature I had been watching, it became a whining, grovelling, incessantly crying baby. This transformation, which can be seen in most nestlings, never fails to interest me. It is not without its parallel in human young, which revert to infantile behaviour in order to obtain the undivided attention of the mother.

Gradually, as the nestling grew up, it began to lose its baby ways and became more adept at feeding itself. Lord Alanbrooke recorded on his film a remarkable demonstration of the process by which the young eagle was taught to feed itself. While the parent was away the nestling picked up a young Rabbit which had been left on the nest. Holding it in its bill it tried first to jerk off some meat. This failing, it then picked up and dropped the carcase repeatedly, with the obvious desire to tear away a portion. It had not however yet learned the necessity of holding the prey in its talons while pulling on it, though producing the correct backward motion of the head in lifting it. At this juncture the adult returned, carrying a recently fledged Magpie. She stood looking at the nestling for a moment. From what follows in the film one might almost believe she then gave a deliberate demonstration of how to pluck and dismember prey. Placing one huge foot on the Magpie, she rapidly and very expertly plucked it, tossing beakfuls of feathers into the air. The nestling watched intently, as though storing up the demonstration for future use. It was then fed. Later in the film the young eagle is seen putting its foot, perhaps accidentally, on its food and thus actually succeeding in tearing off a morsel for itself.

It was a thrilling experience to observe the adult eagle at a distance of only 15 ft. It appeared completely oblivious of the hide, preening itself and even yawning as an indication of its relaxed attitude. The preening was executed with great care and at the conclusion the eagle shook itself like a large dog, with a loud rustling sound, all its feathers standing on end and looking for a moment as though its skin was much too loose for its body. Each time she left the nest the eagle flew just to the left below the hide, within 6 ft. of me, her great wings making a powerful 'whoosh, whoosh' as she passed. While examining her closely through my binoculars I noticed an interesting detail, to which Eric Hosking had already drawn my attention. On the iris of each piercing yellow eye was a concentric pattern of short, dark-brown lines, almost like the abbreviated spokes of a wheel.

We never saw the male at the eyrie, though it was frequently observed with its mate in the neighbouring skies. Once the egg hatched, the male contented itself with bringing food to a favourite tree, where it was received by the female and taken to the nest. The 'food tree' was about 250 yards from the eyrie; when we examined it, a recently killed Hare was found waiting on one of the branches. Beneath the tree were about fifty regurgitated pellets, about $3 \times 1\frac{1}{2}$ in., composed of bones, fur and feathers, which indicated that it was also used as a dormitory. A selection of the pellets was dissected by Tono Valverde, who had been studying food remains at other eyries. These and his other investigations showed that, while Rabbits formed the main bulk of the food, Turtle Doves, Wood Pigeons, Azure-winged Magpie, Magpie, Jackdaw, Black-winged Stilt, Avocet, Wigeon, Gadwall, Mallard, Red-legged Partridge, Cattle Egret, Coot, unidentified sandpipers and terns, and a variety of mammals, were also taken. We collected pellets at roost-trees used by other pairs of Spanish Imperial Eagles. One of these was on the Puntal trail, which we frequently used, and as we rode by in the evenings we sometimes saw the silhouettes of the pair sitting side by side on their favourite branch.

These eagles all too frequently fall victims to local 'sportsmen', though not on the well-protected Coto Doñana, because of their habit of preying on wounded birds. Seventy years ago Abel Chapman complained that they used to follow him about and snatch birds almost at the muzzle of his gun. He shot a number of them, not only in flight, but also at the nest. In his diary of 1883 he protested: 'I never saw such strong birds. They carry off a skinful of heavy shot and unless a wing is broken seem impossible to kill outright.'

Although four species of eagles occur regularly on the Coto, the Spanish Imperials were clearly the dominant birds. They were nevertheless subjected to the mobbing to which all were liable if they incautiously or by design flew close to the breeding grounds of the myriads of terns and waders in the *marismas*. Lapwings and Black-winged Stilts were particularly courageous and packs of them could often be seen dive-bombing an eagle and yelping at it, like small dogs hounding a lordly Great Dane. As a rule the eagle merely took occasional leisurely evasive action; but a Raven which actually struck a Spanish Imperial on the rump caused it to make off at top speed.

I found these eagles much less sluggish than the Imperials of the eastern

XLIX a. Strident-voiced Great Reed Warblers were found nesting very locally in the channel of the Madre de las Marismas

b. The first portrait ever taken of the blue-black Spotless Starling, here shown at its nest hole in an Acacia

L   *a*. A pair of Great Grey Shrikes at the nest. The southern race here shown has a pinkish tint on the breast.   *b*. The colourful Woodchat Shrikes were late breeders, but a picture of the male feeding its mate on the nest was finally obtained

race seen in Asia Minor, which appeared to spend the majority of their time sitting on trees, or even on the ground. There was scarcely a day when we did not observe the Spanish Imperials either quartering the skies on the watch for prey, or indulging in magnificent aerobatics. Play is an essential function to most birds of prey and is part of the training of the young. During all three expeditions we saw adults obviously enjoying games. On one occasion a pair had been circling each other slowly at a great height, as though sparring for an opening; one then succeeded in getting behind the other and immediately a game of tag developed. First one and then the other gained a position from which it could dive on its partner. At the conclusion of the final attack the lower bird rolled over on its back and seized the outstretched talons of the other. Thus interlocked and crying loudly they fell several hundred feet. They then separated, zoomed upwards again and repeated the process with every indication of enjoyment. Such play is, of course, often a 'displacement activity' resulting from human trespass, as James Ferguson-Lees has proved with Peregrines. But some of our observations were made when the eagles were probably unaware of our presence. Other spectacular aerobatics which we saw were the result of territorial conflicts between neighbouring pairs.

Perhaps the most dramatic example of the Spanish Imperial's enjoyment of its mastery of the air occurred one day when a stiff north-easter was blowing across the Coto. I was trudging across the scrub when I heard the familiar 'owk . . . owk' far overhead. Above me a lone eagle was flying at perhaps 2,000 ft. As I watched, it turned half into the wind and began a long descent, gliding at about forty-five degrees, with the wing on the windward side tightly flexed and the other widely spread. In its arrow-like fall, which was at very high speed, it covered perhaps half a mile and cried twenty-eight times at regular intervals. Almost at ground level it soared again, as effortlessly as though jet-propelled. It was impossible not to feel that it was rejoicing in an exhilarating experience.

After my final spell in the eagle hide at the Corral Quemado, I rode away in the comparative cool of the evening, reflecting that in all my travels I had never found so supremely perfect a spot as the Coto Doñana. Almost all the bird families of Europe were not only represented but plentiful. To be able to watch such a rarity as the Spanish Imperial Eagle—and even to take one's pick among several pairs—was incredible fortune. One could erect hides wherever one wished and be certain they would never be disturbed. The terrain, though lacking mountains, was varied and splendidly wild. It was also in many parts beautiful and the ride from the eagle's nest to the *Palacio* was one of my favourites. As my sturdy grey mare picked her way through the shadowy pines, the twin, jewel-like lakes of Sopetón and El Rincón came into view, fringed with emerald green and shining like amethysts under the glowing evening sky. A herd of Fallow Deer was, as usual, grazing there and thirty heads were raised, long ears pricked and limpid eyes wide. Snow-white Little Egrets and Cattle Egrets were feeding near the deer, snapping up frogs and grasshoppers. The water was dotted with a hundred grebes, ducks and coots. Several long-necked Purple Herons stood statuesquely among the reeds, watching me suspiciously. Passing the lakes, the trail led through high clumps of Pistachio, Tree Heath and Genista, where shrikes and warblers abounded. A Cetti's Warbler bobbed up and sang loudly, finishing its song with a ringing '*chewee-cheweeoo*'. Two Nightingales challenged each other and a perky Rufous Warbler, with its large, fox-red tail spread, hopped across from one bush to another. Turning the corner where the arching Brambles made me lean down over my horse's neck, I came suddenly on a tremendous black bull standing in the shade. My horse shied sideways, but the broad, triangular, bullfighter's stirrups saved me from falling. The bull puffed loudly through its nostrils, but let us pass. On we went, now among the lower vegetation, heady with the mixed perfumes of Rosemary, Lavender, Halimium and Camomile. The sandy trail ahead could be read like the pages of a book, criss-crossed as it was by countless tracks. Here the fairy-like footprints of Sand Lizards, there the curving trail of a snake; here passed a Red-legged Partridge, a Dormouse and a Mongoose; beyond was the crafty pit of an Ant Lion larva and the straight, even track the insect left as it 'rowed' its way through the soft surface of the sand.

The white walls of the Casa del Puntal appeared over the rise and I stopped for a cool drink of water from the two-handled earthenware bottle, identical to the amphora of the Phoenicians, which was offered to me by the smiling wife of the *guarda* Curro Chico, who lived there. On the fence around her little vegetable garden a Great Spotted Cuckoo chattered, as it always did whenever we passed that way. Refreshed, I took the trail which wound over the open scrub, on the last lap to the *Palacio*, which I could now see in the distance, gleaming golden-white in the sunset against its dark Eucalyptus trees. Even this part of the journey was full of interest, for the sky was full of birds flying to roost. Every few hundred yards Dartford or Sardinian Warblers popped out of the scrub to sing or to scold. A charcoal burner approached, riding side-saddle on a donkey, his bare feet bobbing in time with his mount's foot-steps. As he passed he wished me a polite *'Buenas tardes, Señor!'* His sad, dark face, swathed in the black head-scarf which many *carboneros* wear, was lit briefly by a friendly smile. Looking back, I saw him gazing stead-fastly at the dying sun, his face again impassive. He began singing quietly to himself, one of those endless, quavering, peasant songs which, as the distance between us increased, seemed to encompass the very essence of Spain's romantic beauty.

Imperial Eagles at play

13

THE 'LITTLE BROWN JOBS'

WITH their native genius for the expressive, the Americans have coined the collective noun 'peep' to embrace the host of small sandpipers and other little waders which crowd the shores and mud-flats of the United States, reserving our word 'waders' chiefly for the larger species. The word 'peep' is onomatopoeic in that nearly all the small shore-birds have call-notes resembling this sound. Faced for the first time in 1952 with the confusing multitude of European warblers, Roger Peterson quickly coined the phrase the 'little brown jobs' to describe them. The expedition members have since given it wide circulation. Perhaps because he had so completely mastered the American 'little brown jobs', of which there are some sixty species, Roger grasped the often very slight diagnostic differences between the various European warblers in an astonishingly short space of time. Before the second expedition was concluded he could excel most of us in speed of their identification, either by voice or appearance.

Thirty-five species of warblers are included on the European breeding list, excluding the accidental American and Asiatic vagrants. Some are very rare, others are normally restricted to the extreme north-east or south-east corners of the continent. It was therefore remarkable that during the three expeditions we identified no fewer than twenty-two different warblers on the Coto Doñana, and a twenty-third species near Jerez. Eleven of these were found to be breeding on the Coto and three more were strongly suspected of doing so.

At the time of our visits the typical warblers of the dry scrub regions, among Halimium, Gorse and Bramble patches, were the Dartford, the Sardinian and the Whitethroat, the last-named being chiefly a passage migrant, thought a few were breeding. In 1952 the Sardinian Warbler was unquestionably the most plentiful of the three. In 1956 and 1957 its numbers were much diminished, perhaps because, being a winter resident, it had suffered severe losses during the exceptional frosts in the winter of 1955–6. It is an early breeder; I saw young on the wing at the end of April in 1952 and 1956. The Dartfords (which are also winter residents) were the most numberous scrub warblers of 1956 and 1957. The Subalpine Warbler, which bred on the Coto in Abel Chapman's day, and may still do so, was recorded by us only as a scarce passage migrant on all three expeditions. The Spectacled Warbler was evidently breeding in very small numbers and a group of six was located among Gorse and Brambles in 1957; some were feeding young. The Lesser Whitethroat, which Jourdain (1936) referred to as 'a very rare straggler to the southern provinces of Spain', was observed by us only in 1956, when two or three migrants were seen near the coast on 13 May.

Turning to the other members of the *Sylviidae*, Blackcaps and Garden Warblers were noted each year as passage migrants, the former, which possibly nests on the Coto, varying from one to four records each year and the latter from a dozen to twenty. A few of the handsome Orphean Warblers were seen on migration, and some settled to breed, in the Pinar de San Agustin and the Corral de la Cita. The sites were appropriate, in high undergrowth among pines. There is no mistaking this large warbler, with its extensive black cap and conspicuous white eye-ring. We heard a number of males singing regularly, their repeated, Rock-Thrush-like phrases suggesting that nesting territories had been established.

There were two *Hippolais* warblers, the Melodious and the Olivaceous. The former, a beautiful bird, with lemon-yellow breast and high-crowned appearance, was our constant companion whenever we were in the moister, bushy parts of the Coto. Its almost interminable warbling was remarkably sweet, though not very loud. In numbers this was one of the most important warblers of the Coto. It is a rather late breeder and migratory parties were still passing through as late as the second week in May. I found a delicately woven hammock nest being built, chiefly of leaf particles, moss and spiders' webs, in the top of a Bramble bush on 23 May. Tono Valverde told me that the nests on the Coto were usually just below eye-level and almost invariably in Brambles. The rather nondescript Olivaceous Warbler, which in form and behaviour resembles the Melodious Warbler, breeds only in south-eastern Europe and the southern parts of Spain. It has a rather larger bill than the Melodious, but completely lacks the latter's clear yellow and greenish coloration, being a dull mouse-brown with a buffish-white breast. The songs are however completely dissimilar, that of the Olivaceous being more akin to a vigorous Sedge Warbler's. We heard no full song on the Coto, though a few of the migrants gave tongue briefly and may have nested later. The peak of the migratory movement appeared to be during the first week of May. There was no evidence of breeding by the end of the month and there seemed to be few suitable habitats available except perhaps in the *Palacio* vegetable garden or around some of the ponds, for this is a species generally preferring lush vegetation in cultivated areas.

The *Acrocephalus* warblers were represented on the Coto chiefly by the strident-voiced Great Reed Warbler, which was locally common in suitable reed-beds, as, for example, along the channel of the Madre. We found nests with incomplete clutches on 22 May 1957. In previous years, when the *marismas* had normal water levels, we had been unable to penetrate to the Madre and thus saw only single birds on migration. Single records of Reed and Marsh Warblers were obtained; a few of the former breed on the Coto, but the latter was obviously a vagrant, as its normal breeding range does not include the Iberian peninsula.

Four warblers of the *Phylloscopus* family were identified during the expeditions, the Bonelli's, the Willow, the Chiffchaff and the Wood Warbler. The last-mentioned species, seen by Roger Peterson and me on 8 May 1956, was a single bird on migration. It perched in full view with a mixed party of wagtails on a fence at Algaida—a thoroughly unlikely spot for a woodland species. The Bonelli's Warbler was fairly frequently seen on the Coto during our visits, though Jourdain claimed in 1936 that it had not yet occurred there. Although most of those we saw were probably on migration, I suspect that some remained to breed, as territories were held in a few appropriate sites within half a mile of the *Palacio* and in the Corral de la Cita. Although in habitat and song rather similar to the Wood Warbler, the Bonelli's looks more like a white-breasted Chiffchaff with an inconspicuous yellowish patch on the rump. The song is quite easily distinguished from the trill of the Wood Warbler, being slower and *on the same note*, without the typical descending scale and acceleration of the latter's song. A few Chiffchaffs and/or Willow Warblers were seen on migration as late as the second and even the third weeks in May. The Spanish race of the Chiffchaff (*P. c. ibericus*) even more closely resembles the Willow Warbler than does our more northern race; it was usually impossible to distinguish the two species with certainty in the field. Unless therefore very close observation was possible, or the songs were heard, our recorders put them down as 'Willow-Chiffs', which seemed a wise precaution. Judging again by Jourdain's notes, that spring migration of these species through Andalucía occurred 'in March and early April', either his observation was at fault or the movements we saw were remarkably late.

We now come to four miscellaneous warblers, each representing a different genus—*Cettia*, *Locustella*, *Cisticola* and *Agrobates*. The small, skulking Cetti's Warbler was seen only three or four times on each expedition. It is a difficult bird to flush, but its song is unmistakable, being particularly loud; the chief phrase is a characteristic, repeated *'chewee'*, or *'cheweeoo'*. Eric Hosking, Max Nicholson and I heard this loud call coming from some Pistachio and Bramble bushes one day and, although we searched for fifteen minutes and the bird sang repeatedly, all we saw was a brief glimpse of a small red-brown form with a short, rounded tail, diving swiftly from one bush to another. Others were seen later in the Soto Grande (where they are known to nest) and in the Coto del Rey regions. The Savi's Warbler, which is related to our Grasshopper Warbler, more nearly resembles a Reed Warbler in appearance. It is not numerous on the Coto, though it breeds in the *Juncus* rushes around some of the lakes and at El Higuerón and El Hondón. James Ferguson-Lees found our first nest by the Sopetón lake on 6 May 1957. It was carefully concealed among the stems of a clump of *Juncus* rushes about 18 in. above the water; one could stand within inches of the nest without spotting it. Very careful inspection showed it to contain five pinkish eggs. The site was immediately put 'out of bounds' to further inspection until 8 May when the nest was found to have been destroyed, in such a manner as to suggest the culprit was a bird rather than an animal—probably a Magpie or a Purple Heron, both of which frequented the site. On 10 May the Savi's Warbler was seen in the same place and on the 18th a new nest with three eggs was discovered by Tony Miller. Scrupulous care was taken not to disturb the vegetation nor to leave tracks to the nest and again the site was denied to further observation for some days. On 28 May it was visited and we found that the first egg had hatched. On 30 May Eric Hosking and Lord Alanbrooke photographed and filmed the parents at the nest and John Parrinder made sound recordings of their voices (*see* Plate XLVI).

Among the most typical birds of the Andalusian lowlands are the minute Fan-tailed Warblers. They can be seen in their characteristic, deeply undulating flight over the corn-fields, meadows and marshes everywhere. They frequently fly very high in a most un-warbler-like manner and can then be located only by their repeated '*dzeep . . . dzeep*' call-notes. On the Coto they occur in some numbers along the edges of the *marismas* and around most of the lakes. Like the Savi's, they hide their nests extremely well. Our field parties spent many hours searching and finally, on 19 May 1957, Tony and James found one near the Sopetón lake. It was exquisitely constructed and purse-shaped, resembling a long cocoon, or an ear of Maize. The *Carex* sedges had been brought together 12 in. from the ground and bound with copious layers of spiders' web so cunningly and tightly that one could scarcely believe there was room for the nest. The small opening near the top of the purse was just large enough to permit the bird to enter head downwards. There were

LI *a*. The most colourful birds of the Coto Doñana were undoubtedly the Bee-eaters, several colonies of which were found nesting in tunnels dug in flat ground. *b*. A resplendent male Golden Oriole feeding young in its hammock-shaped nest

four minute eggs and these hatched successfully on 23 May. As soon as the parents had settled to feeding the young regularly, a hide was erected and excellent films and portraits were obtained (*see* Plate XLVII). The film showed that when feeding the nestlings the parents were obliged to come out of the narrow nest backwards. Close study of Eric Hosking's photographs showed that the principal food of the young was the larvae of one of the Bush Crickets (*Decticinae*).

The twenty-second warbler species seen on the Coto, the rather flamboyant Rufous Warbler, was observed in fair numbers on all three expeditions, on the final occasion being sighted some twenty times, once in a party of seven. Again we judged that the majority were migrants, but nests are said to have been found on the Coto and there are a few hedges of Prickly Pear cactus, their favourite nest site, which might have been used after we departed. The Rufous Warbler is an exotic. It is a big, strikingly coloured warbler, its most notable feature being its large, fox-red tail, which is boldly tipped with black and white. It feeds chiefly on the ground among bushes, hopping about on its rather long legs and jerking its long tail not only vertically but often right up over its back. In behaviour it is bold and perky and in every way quite unlike our dainty woodland and garden warblers. During the war I saw three birds of the eastern race (*Agrobates galactotes syriacus*—often called the Brown-backed Warbler) squabbling like vulgar House Sparrows in a cactus hedge around a military depot in the Middle East. They even came to pick at half an orange which I tossed to them.

One more warbler apparently occurs on the Coto from time to time: the Moustached Warbler. We failed to find it there, but it was seen near Jerez by the 1952 expedition and is said to have been observed on or very near the Coto in 1956 and 1957.

Although strictly speaking not 'little brown jobs' in Roger's sense of the phrase, some of the other small birds of the Coto may conveniently be mentioned in this chapter.

Nightingales were very numerous, particularly in 1952 when they seemed to be singing from every thicket and were often found in Bramble patches even in the drier localities. Great Tits were well distributed but in small numbers, breeding chiefly in Cork Oaks and around the *Palacio* and huts. Blue Tits were even less numerous. We saw no Crested or Long-tailed Tits on the Coto, though they were observed on the other side of the river, as were Robins, Short-toed Tree Creepers and Firecrests.

Large numbers of Pied Flycatchers were seen on migration each year. I counted 200 in a small plantation of pines one afternoon in the first week of May 1956. Spotted Flycatchers also were observed in flocks, but in smaller numbers. A single Collared Flycatcher was seen by John Raines on 22 May 1957; this species breeds chiefly in the eastern half of Europe and the record was an unusual one. Two migrant Meadow Pipits and a dozen Tree Pipits were observed in 1956 and four of the latter in 1957. Tawny Pipits were less numerous than we expected, though we recorded a few on each expedition. Redstarts and Whinchats came through fairly frequently, usually with other small migrants. A few Stonechats were breeding, two families of young being seen just out of the nest in 1956 and four in 1957; they are rather more numerous to the north-west of the Coto. The Black Redstart and Wren were seen only once.

Although Blackbirds were resident and nesting in small numbers, chiefly among the higher undergrowth under pines, we all missed the familiar Song Thrush, which is so typical of most of Europe; in Spain the southern boundary of its range does not extend farther south than about the level of the north of Portugal. Mistle Thrushes, on the other hand, breed down to the southern extremity of Spain and we saw one or two in 1952 and 1957 around Jerez. The typical *Turdidae* of the southern highlands are the colourful Rock Thrush and Blue Rock Thrush; two females of the former were recorded as migrants on the Coto in 1956 and both species were seen among the *sierras* in 1957. Their smaller relatives the Wheatear and Black-eared Wheatear were observed on migration on the Coto; nests of the latter and of the very handsome Black Wheatear were found on rocky ground within about fifty miles of Jerez.

Among the seed-eating species, the Goldfinch was the most numerous representative on the Coto. Only four Chaffinches were seen, at the peak of the migratory movement in 1956, though they were breeding on the other side of the river. One or two Greenfinches were noted each year, but they were apparently not resident. Serins were not recorded until 1957, when several were heard singing and two parties of young were seen. A very strange record was of two or possibly three undoubted Siskins seen by James Fisher and James Ferguson-Lees in a coastal oasis near Matalascañas on 8 May 1956, an exceptionally late date. A party of twenty Yellowhammers passed through the Coto with some Ortolan Buntings on 2 May of the same year; this also was an unusually interesting occurrence, as the species is normally only a winter vagrant to Andalucía. We saw no Hawfinches, though Philip Hollom had recorded two in March 1938 in the north of the Coto and they are sometimes plentiful in the pine woods in winter. Ortolan Buntings were seen as migrants in 1956 and 1957. I watched a pair in 1952 which gave every indication of having a nest, but without gaining conclusive evidence of breeding; Abel Chapman said Ortolans bred on the larger grassy islands in the *marismas* in his day. A few pairs of Corn Buntings certainly nest locally and we found one or two singing on obviously well-established territories. We saw only one Reed Bunting, possibly a migrant, in 1956, though Chapman again used to find their nests in the *marismas*.

House Sparrows were of course nesting in the *Palacio* and in some of the huts and I saw a pair of Tree Sparrows investigating an occupied Spotless Starlings' nest-hole in an Acacia tree outside the *Palacio* in 1956; this was our only record for this species. No trace was found of the interesting Spanish Sparrow *Passer hispaniolensis*, though I had seen a few between Jerez and Sevilla in 1952. They used to breed on the Coto in Chapman's time. They are chiefly birds of the woodland glades of Spain, frequently breeding in the foundations of the nests of storks and eagles. The only place where I have found them breeding in buildings was in Morocco, where a colony had taken over old nests of House Martins and Red-rumped Swallows under the arches of a mosque at Marrakech.

I asked James Ferguson-Lees to summarize the migratory movements observed during the 1956 and 1957 expeditions. The following is extracted from his report:

'An examination of the weather charts for southern Spain and Morocco shows that the spring migration probably needs a certain combination of easterly winds and other factors of the weather to bring the northward-moving migrants through the Coto Doñana. If the wind and weather are not just right, the majority of them pass farther east, having crossed the Strait of Gibraltar at its narrowest point, or, when the winds are westerly, having been blown a corresponding distance to the east. This may suggest that it is a question of luck whether one sees any migrants on the Coto or not, and this is true to a large extent. But the right set of weather conditions seems to occur fairly frequently at that time of year and in each of our visits we had interesting 'rushes' of migrants on several days. In 1956 we were fortunate enough to arrive at a time when no migration was taking place: this meant that we started with a clean sheet, as it were. When, nearly three days later, on 1 May, a heavy movement started, we were able to watch it develop from the very beginning. This movement was particularly of Spotted Flycatchers and, a day later, of Pied Flycatchers; with them were Redstarts, Whinchats, many warblers, and a few Golden Orioles, Rollers, Ortolan Buntings and Wheatears. This passage, which really began in earnest on 2 May, had dropped right away by the 4th, but on the 6th another spectacular movement had started; this lasted until the 8th, to be succeeded by another wave on the 12th and 13th. In each case the development was the same. The arrival of a few migrants in the *Palacio* garden, always a favoured area, would be the signal that a rush was on. The next day it would be possible to find twenty or thirty flycatchers and a host of other birds in almost any of the many Cork Oaks and Stone Pines dotted across the open parts of the Coto. But the most spectacular places to see the migrants are the small *corrales* or pine woods in the desert near the coast, where they rest before passing inland. One of these little "oases" at Matalascañas, for example, was always worth a visit if there was any migration taking place. This area is one of low scrub, perhaps of 200 × 300 yards, dotted with forty or fifty widely scattered dwarf Stone Pines and a few Junipers. None of these pines is more than 8 or 9 ft. tall, yet they become simply alive with tired birds, which are most reluctant to leave the meagre shelter. One can sit down at a distance of 4 or 5 yards, even closer at times, and identify a significant proportion of the contents of the *Field Guide* at leisure—and it is leisure that one needs, for at a peak rush there can be as many as twenty or thirty small birds in one of these tiny pines. On one occasion George Shannon and I had ten species of warblers in two adjacent trees: Melodious, Olivaceous, Orphean, Garden, Whitethroat, Subalpine, Rufous, Willow, Bonelli's and a single Great Reed Warbler, which looked very out of place perched in a desert pine. There were also flycatchers, Redstarts and a Woodchat Shrike in the same trees, for good measure.

'In 1957 we watched a similar pattern take place during 5, 6, 13, 15, 21 and 22 May; but we did not arrive until the 5th, and we came then in the middle of what was probably the last big movement of the spring.

'I have mentioned only the migration of the passerine birds, but a word must also be said about the very spectacular movements of Black Terns, which took place in 1956 during 3, 5, 7 and 8 May, and to a lesser extent on a few days subsequently. On these dates there was a continuous passage of these birds, presumably heading for their breeding grounds in northern Europe, at a time when the local Black Terns had already hatched their eggs. On 3 May, for example, in a matter of one hour, some 3,000 Black Terns arrived at the Laguna de Santa Olalla, circled and passed on. On other days parties of ten to seventy flew steadily northwards over our heads wherever we were on the Coto, every three to ten minutes, for hours on end. Fantastic numbers must have passed through on a broad front at that time.'

14

A GALAXY OF BIRDS

S OME impression of the richness of the bird-life of the Coto Doñana in spring may be gathered from the fact that during the first eight days of May 1956 we recorded a total of 158 different species. On five occasions the daily totals exceeded 100. On 8 May 113 species were seen. By the end of three weeks we had found in this relatively small and completely flat area no fewer than 171 different species, or more than one-third of the total occurring throughout the whole of Europe. The following year we saw 168 species, of which 22 were additional to the 1956 list, making a total of 193 for the two expeditions. During our explorations on the other side of the river and in the adjacent *sierras* we identified a further 29 species, giving a grand total of 222 seen within fifty miles of the *Palacio* between mid-April and mid-June. If one added the many other species occurring during autumn migration, this figure for the area would obviously be even greater.

On the night of 3 May 1956, when the day's reports were being entered in the official log-book, I noticed that the members of the field party for the day were in a state of barely concealed excitement. It had been another big day for migratory movement and birds had been arriving during the night in great numbers. It was not until we came towards the end of the list that the cause of the excitement was revealed. It was then announced that John Parrinder and Eric Hosking had clearly seen, in two widely separated areas, a species never before recorded in Spain—the Masked Shrike *Lanius nubicus*. This very striking bird is a resident of Greece, southern Jugoslavia and Asia Minor, wintering in north-east Africa and Arabia. Howard Saunders thought he saw one in Gibraltar in 1873. Almost certainly two different birds were concerned in our Coto Doñana records. The first was seen at the Casa del Puntal; the other, later in the day, was at a spot four miles away. The following day James Fisher and James Ferguson-Lees sighted one of these birds again at the Casa del Puntal. All the field notes made at the time mentioned the long black tail, with white outer feathers, the very black crown and contrasting white forehead and the reddish flanks. The Masked Shrike is about the size of a Woodchat and has closely similar oval white patches on its black wings, but it lacks the latter's white rump and chestnut crown. One of the birds was observed to be carrying nesting material, but although a painstaking search was made, no trace either of a nest or of a mate was found. It was particularly interesting that on both occasions the Masked Shrikes were seen in company with migrating flocks of Pied Flycatchers, whose black and white markings and white foreheads bear more than a superficial resemblance to the plumage pattern of these birds.

The behaviour of the Woodchat Shrikes puzzled us considerably. On all three expeditions we arrived in the latter part of April to find the Coto swarming with them. Many were already singing from fence posts and the tops of bushes, in a manner which we interpreted as the first stages of settling to breed, particularly as the same perches were occupied for several days. On one occasion I was able to count no fewer than seven of these birds sitting on the tops of Bramble clumps, without moving my binoculars. Both Chapman (1906) and Jourdain (1936) referred to this species as an abundant and widely distributed summer resident in Andalucía. Jourdain went on to say that by the middle of May nests could be found in profusion. Yet we could not find a single nest on the Coto until 1957. From the last week of April to the first week of May 1956, Woodchats swarmed throughout the Coto, but on 10 May, during the long ride from the *Palacio* to Algaida and back, only one was seen. During the following week only seventeen were counted on all our extensive travels throughout the region. In spite of the misleading behaviour of those seen previously, it was evident that they had merely been birds of passage. This was borne out by the fact that small groups of Woodchats were noted during May among the various migrants in the oases of vegetation on the coast. Lady Alanbrooke finally located a breeding pair for us towards the end of the 1957 expedition. The nest was found on 26 May and the birds photographed and filmed on eggs on 30 May. Doubtless others nested on the Coto later in June, but in view of the fact that our expeditions covered three different breeding seasons, with a normal spring, a late spring and a drought, Jourdain's observations suggest that the Woodchat has since adopted a later period for reproduction in this area.

One might assume that the Great Grey Shrike would be more conspicuous than its small cousin the Woodchat, on account of the much larger area of its shining white breast (*see* Plate L). On the contrary, we found it remarkably self-effacing while breeding. I never succeeded in flushing a sitting bird; always she slipped quietly away through the back of the bush. Once the young have left the nest, however, the parents become bolder and scold the intruder with a variety of wheezing, rasping and squealing cries. We found six nests during each of our expeditions and several broods just out of the nest; the breeding season therefore appears to be chiefly in April and May. The Great Grey Shrike apparently prefers to nest chiefly in dense Brambles near or among scattered trees, whereas the Woodchat has a preference for building in low trees in more open localities.

I spent three days studying Great Grey Shrikes at their nests. Seen from the hide the very beautiful rosy tint on the breasts of the adults, which is characteristic of this southern race (*Lanius excubitor meridionalis*), was clearly visible, though it can seldom be seen at normal observational range. The food given to the young consisted chiefly of Sand Lizards *Psammodromus algirus*, shrews (probably *Suncus etruscus*), Mole Crickets *Gryllotalpa gryllotalpa* and a variety of beetles. One of the tiger moths was also brought to the nest. On one occasion Roger saw the female shrike bring a lizard fully 5 in. in length. After trying unsuccessfully to make

LII *a*. A Bee-eater poses on a picturesque skull, while holding in its bill a Striped Hawk Moth. *b*. When digging its underground nest hole the Bee-eater supports itself on its wings and kicks back the sand with a rapid pedalling motion

two different nestlings swallow it, she rammed it down the throat of a third; this chick, although scarcely 3 in. in length, gulped it down. In less than ten seconds the tip of the lizard's tail had disappeared. Within twenty minutes the nestling was fed again. What an accommodating digestive system birds have!

Perhaps the most interesting discovery I made at the Great Grey Shrikes' nests was that the adults can produce a clappering noise with their bills, exactly like the White Stork in miniature. The male did this repeatedly at one nest, not only when perched but also in flight while circling around the nest-tree. The performance appeared to be in the nature of an indication of disquiet or mild alarm, not of greeting. Each period of clappering lasted usually for three to five seconds, though on one occasion I timed a spell of ten seconds. The delivery was, of course, much more rapid than the equivalent of the White Stork. Twice I heard the male accelerate the rate towards the end of the performance. I photographed the male shrike at the moment of clappering and my picture clearly showed its bill to be wide open.

As I was experimenting during this expedition with the reactions of various nesting birds to the local brood-parasitic species (the Cuckoo and Great Spotted Cuckoo), I decided to see what would happen if I attached mounted specimens near the nest of a Great Grey Shrike. There was no reaction whatever to a stuffed Cuckoo, which is a rather uncommon bird on the Coto, but a stuffed Great Spotted Cuckoo evoked signs of considerable anxiety from both parents. They did not return to the nest for an hour, but sat on the adjacent Pistachio bushes, sounding two different anxiety notes, 'jhit' and 'jhittock', both quietly delivered. There was no aggressive reaction. Not wishing to keep them from their hungry nestlings, I then removed the stuffed bird. I was, however, interested to learn that, although the Great Spotted Cuckoo has never been known to parasitize shrikes, it was evidently regarded as a potential enemy, both by this species and by the Woodchat Shrike; the latter dive-bombed the stuffed bird repeatedly. This cuckoo is very common on the Coto and its rather hawk-like shape must make it suspect to smaller birds.

LIII A Hoopoe, with its fine crest lowered, taking a small lizard to its nestlings. The nest is in an empty bee-hive made of slabs of bark from a Cork Oak

Although we found no 'larders' of the Great Grey Shrike on the Coto, this species is known to impale shrews, lizards, small birds and beetles on thorns, as a reserve food supply, in the same manner as is done by our familiar Red-backed Shrike in England. I must confess that I always find shrikes faintly disquieting birds. On the one hand one sees ample evidence of their ferocity as hunters and this impression is heightened by the sight of their sharply hooked bills and the discovery of their still living prey squirming on the thorns of their 'larders'. On the other, one is spellbound by the sweetness and amazing variety of their songs, into which they weave an unlimited mimicry of the notes of other birds. Their behaviour at the nest also gives one an impression of unusual parental solicitude. For example, when one of the nestlings I was watching clambered out of the nest and pushed its head between the legs of its parent, in an attempt to make her brood, she gently pushed it back into the nest with the top of her head. These impressions of actions for which there are quite simple biological explanations are, admittedly, unreasonably anthropomorphic, but sometimes they are difficult to avoid.

In the eyes of visiting British naturalists the gorgeously coloured Bee-eater is probably the most spectacular bird of the Coto. My portrait on Plate LI does it less than justice. It is of course very common in the south of Spain, in spite of frequent persecution. Unfortunately these lovely creatures are far from shy and readily establish breeding colonies in roadside cuttings, embankments and sand quarries, where the local peasant boys can amuse themselves by catching or catapulting them. In 1952 we found a colony in a sand-pit near Jerez, where every nest-hole had a horsehair noose set in the entrance. On another occasion we found a wounded Bee-eater suspended by the neck to a fence post, while a group of barefooted urchins sat around it waiting to kill other birds attracted by its struggles. Such brutality to a bird of gentle temperament and exquisite beauty is difficult to understand, but I have seen worse offences committed by Arab children in North Africa. The erroneous belief that Bee-eaters subsist entirely on honey bees may be the chief cause of their persecution. This is, of course, not true, for they often eat many more beetles, butterflies and dragonflies; but, in default of any means of educating the Spanish peasants in the conservation of their country's wonderful fauna, the senseless slaughter will probably continue unabated.

As the Coto Doñana is so rich in insect life, and particularly in dragonflies, it did not surprise us to find that Bee-eaters were plentiful. With the exception of the sand dunes, however, the whole area is as flat as the proverbial billiard table and no suitable nesting sites appeared to be available. Not to be out-done, the Bee-eaters made good the deficiency by digging their tunnels in level open ground, as has been reported from some other countries. In 1957 the recession of the *marismas*, with their attendant insect multitudes, forced the Bee-eaters to nest far out on what the previous year had been the bed of a lake. The sandy, grass-covered mud had already been baked by the sun to such a hard consistency that we had to use a heavy mallet and an iron spike to make the holes for our hide poles; but the Bee-eaters somehow managed to penetrate it with their slender bills and puny feet. First they dug vertically downward for about 4 in., then horizontally, just below the surface.

In 1956 we found five colonies, each of twenty-five to thirty pairs, the largest being near the Martinazo hut. The first scrapes were noticed on 30 April. By 3 May, although there was still much tentative digging here and there, many holes had been finally adopted and had progressed as much as 9 in. A hole 15 in. in length was found caved-in by a passing cow; we placed a dry cow-pat over the demolition and the birds continued tunnelling. Copulation and courtship feeding were now seen frequently. By 16 May all the pairs had deep holes and were hard at work. We did not ascertain the final depths attained, but there are records of holes in banks having reached the astonishing depth of 9 ft., and Abel Chapman measured one in the flat ground of the Coto which was exactly 10 ft. long. Judging from the furious intensity with which Bee-eaters work, it is not surprising that their tunnels are often far deeper than appears to be strictly necessary. The depth is, however, no protection against the entry of the Ocellated Lizard, the Mongoose, rats and various snakes, all of which play havoc with the eggs and young birds.

The tunnelling was fascinating to watch. Both sexes took part and divided the task about equally. It was essentially a matter of team work. The waiting bird always stood right at the entrance, where it was repeatedly smothered by the sand which was kicked from the hole in a vigorous spray by the digging bird. The instant the latter backed out, its mate dived underground. The relieved bird then flew briefly, shaking the dust from its feathers, and circled back to the nest. The digging bird always kept up a running commentary of muffled notes, which were eagerly answered from above. Sometimes the waiting bird was so impatient to take part that it began scraping rapidly with its feet before entering the hole (see Plate LIIb). While digging, the Bee-eater first hammers the face of the tunnel with its bill, which becomes noticeably worn down by the time the work is completed; it then leans forward on its breast and the butts of its wings, while its tiny feet kick the soil out backwards with a rapid running motion. This is done with such energy that the jets of sand fly through the air for a distance of 3 ft. and leave a conspicuous fan-shaped patch outside each nest.

The Bee-eaters were charmingly tame. While I was in my hide one perched on the corner just above my head, to shake the dust from its feathers. It was pleasant to hear its throaty call-notes so closely. Roger Peterson filmed a pair courtship-feeding on the picturesque skull of a cow which lay near the nest, and Eric Hosking obtained a splendid portrait of the male on the skull with a Striped Hawk-moth *Celerio livornica* in its bill. Other food included dragonflies, beetles, Clouded Yellow Butterflies and various species of wild bees. We noticed that the spells of digging were at their height in late morning and afternoon; we did not, however, make any observations early in the morning, when there would probably be another peak of activity. Occasionally the whole colony appeared to receive some kind of signal and every pair would leave the ground simultaneously and in complete silence and fly far away. This behaviour was analogous to the sudden so-called 'dreads' which occur in tern colonies when, without apparent reason, every bird silently takes wing. Each time this took place I examined the surroundings carefully, expecting to see a predator of some kind, but I never obtained a clue to the alarm. After a few minutes the beautiful chorus of soft, purring notes 'prrut', or 'prruik', would be heard and the pairs settled at their holes again. In the brilliant sunlight their vivid electric-blue breasts, yellow throats, rich chestnut backs and blue-green wings and tails were a magnificent sight against the patches of purple Dwarf Bugloss and white Camomile which carpeted the ground.

Hoopoes were less numerous than we had expected from the presence of so many hollow trees on the Coto. The very few pairs we located were evidently hard-pressed to find accommodation not already pre-empted by Jackdaws. However, we finally found a nest in 1956 in an original site—a disused bee-hive outside the Algaida hut. The hive was constructed of three slabs of bark from a Cork Oak, roughly pegged together. The entrance hole was just beneath the roof. On the straw floor lay eight downy nestlings and one infertile egg. Pieces of grey-green egg-shell surrounded the young birds. There were no nest materials. The parents accepted a hide near the nest without hesitation and we obtained some splendid pictures. Before entering the nest the male perched on a fence a few feet away, then flew to the hive, with the typically floppy, butterfly-like action of its rounded and heavily barred black and white wings. Usually it clung to the entrance hole for a few seconds, supporting itself woodpecker-fashion on its widely spread tails before entering. (see Plate LIII). Lizards and Mole Crickets were the only food given to the young. The male Hoopoe was particularly co-operative to the photographers and Roger was able to take a splendid film sequence when Eric, in an adjacent hide, imitated its deep 'poo-poo-poo' call-note. Still holding an orange Mole Cricket in its long bill, the Hoopoe raised its glorious fan-shaped crest, inflated its throat and answered repeatedly, while Roger kept his cinematograph camera turning. It was a delightful incident for our film. Unfortunately the beehive nest was later overturned and the young killed by one of the ever-hungry *podencos* (hunting dogs).

The following year we found another nest containing a family of fledged young Hoopoes, just beneath the cork strips laid along the roof of a straw *choza* in a field of corn. Lord Alanbrooke just had time to make a film before some of them flew. They were recovered and put back in the nest, where they remained for a while. Handling young Hoopoes is not a pleasant task, for, like the adult female, they can secrete a foul-smelling liquid from their perineal glands as a protective device. They have paler plumage than their parents and shorter bills. We heard them piping a thin high note while sitting on fence posts waiting to be fed.

Rollers, like the Hoopoes, were late arrivals on the Coto. We saw about a dozen of these handsome birds each year. A party of four was sighted on the coast, obviously exhausted by their flight across the sea; when we approached, one bird could only just manage to fly a few yards before pitching again. A Roller at Martinazo was seen to be picking up sticks, but it did not carry them and we found no evidence of breeding on any of our expeditions, though the species is thought to have nested on the Coto in the past. It is indeed doubtful whether any now breed there, as Jackdaws, which have multiplied at such an amazing rate in the past decade, leave no holes unoccupied. The Roller is one of my favourite birds of the south and there are few more splendid sights than this rather heavy, Jay-like creature, with its pale azure-blue head and breast, chestnut back and bright blue and black wings. It earns its name by its acrobatic nuptial display, 'tumbling' and twisting in flight to impress its mate.

Another of the Coto Doñana's spectacular birds is the Azure-winged Magpie, a cousin of our common Magpie. It is now locally numerous, though chiefly confined to the Stone Pine woods and Eucalyptus groves. Abel Chapman remarked in 1910 that he had never seen one farther south than Sevilla and that the species was completely unknown on the Coto in his day. We found several colonies between the Corral de la Cita and the river and near El Rocío. All the nests which we examined were at a height of between 9 and 16 ft., usually in the main forks or crowns of the pines. They were constructed of pine twigs, thickly lined with vegetable fibres, Red Deer hair and tufts of Hare and Rabbit fur. The maximum clutch appeared to be eight buffish eggs, heavily zoned at the large end and with ash-grey markings and with a few dark spots scattered over the remainder of the shell. The Azure-winged Magpie is not usually easy to observe closely, being very alert and quick in its movements. I did however manage in 1952 to stalk a party of twenty-six which was feeding among fresh deer droppings in a woodland clearing. Their deportment marked them clearly as relations of the Magpie, as they strutted perkily about, with tails held high. These birds have very white throats and jet-black caps, extending below the eye to the cheek and nape; their wings and very long, graduated tails are powder blue, making a delicate contrast with their pinkish-grey bodies. In flight the wing-beats are rapid but shallow. The call-notes are noisy and querulous, the most characteristic cry being a hoarse, rising 'zhree'. This very interesting and beautiful bird is found nowhere in Europe except the southern half of Spain and Portugal; one has to go as far as eastern Asia to find the only other known population. It is therefore important that the precious remnant of the European birds should be given adequate protection.

We succeeded in 1957 in photographing and filming a pair of Azure-winged Magpies at their nest in a Stone Pine in the Corral de la Cita. To do so we built a small pylon against an adjacent tree and mounted the hide high enough to permit the cameras to obtain clear views into the nest. It was a difficult site, as the dense canopy of pine needles kept nearly all the light from our subject. Moreover the cock bird insisted always in hiding all but its head behind a thick branch while feeding the young. The female, however, approached invariably from the more exposed side of the nest and occasionally stood in full view while waiting for the young to defecate. Considering the conditions, Eric Hosking's pictures were remarkably good (see Plate VIIa). Once again we were making history, for this species had never previously been photographed.

When first we saw them, the chicks had not yet opened their eyes. We continued our observations until the day they left the nest and so obtained a detailed record of their development. They were fed exclusively by regurgitation, so we had no opportunity to ascertain the exact nature of their food.

A week before the young left the nest I spent a day in the hide; in spite of their usually cautious behaviour the parents had become so accustomed to it that they returned to the nest within five minutes and fed the young twelve times in the first hour. Unlike most regurgitating species, which bring up food with the head lowered, the parents held their heads slightly above the horizontal to do so, opening their bills widely. The young were by then extremely active and kept up a constant clamour for food. While the parents were absent the food calls were loud and not unlike a shortened and weaker version of the typical adult '*zhree*' note. As soon as a parent came to the nest, however, the young adopted a much fainter, but quicker, cheeping note. The parents roused them to feed with a very quiet '*ker*', when within 2 ft. of the nest. The youngsters were remarkably pretty, with pale blue wings and blackish primaries, dark, speckled crowns, white throats and pale, greyish-pink upper parts. Seeking an accurate simile for the colour of their backs, I found I could not get beyond 'mutation mink'! When they stretched open their mouths for food, I could see that their gapes were a vivid shade of crimson, the flanges of their bills being pale pink.

John Parrinder and I had another interesting day at this nest, obtaining sound recordings of the various noises made by the parents and nestlings. We then experimented with a stuffed Eagle Owl placed on a perch near the nest-tree, to see if John could record the alarm notes, while I tried to photograph the Azure-winged Magpies mobbing the owl. John succeeded admirably, but the huge Eagle Owl was evidently too much for the parents, which refused to come nearer than the surrounding trees. We did however attract two other pairs, which joined with 'our' birds in an interesting chorus of alarm cries. These took three forms: a high, urgent, squeaky note, which I jotted down phonetically as '*quer*'; a lower, more grating note '*zhre*', shorter than the typical call-note; and a buzzing, churring note, not unlike the rattling alarm of a Mistle Thrush.

Another enchanting inhabitant of the Coto which, both for its colours and for its magnificent voice, deserves special mention is the Golden Oriole. There is something about the male's exceptional sleekness and shining gold and black plumage which reminds me of an oriental figurine.

184

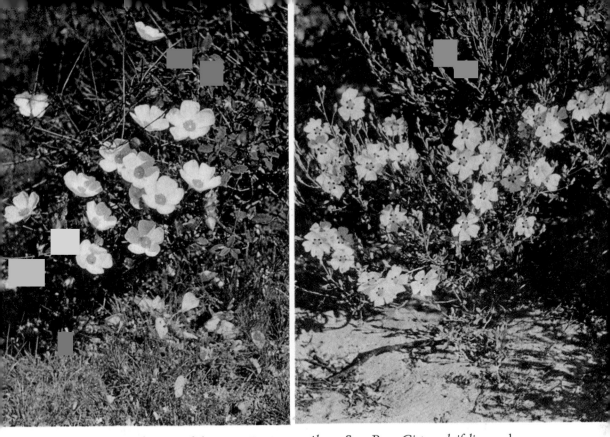

LIV   Some flowers of the Coto Doñana.   *Above:* Sun–Rose *Cistus salvifolius,* and *Halimium halimifolium,* a close relative of the Rock–Rose.   *Below:* Prickly Pear Cactus *Opuntia monacantha,* and Sun–Rose *Cistus crispus*

The Golden Oriole is the dandy of the bird world and it is unthinkable that it should ever have a feather out of place (*see* Plate LI). The sight of a flock of males swooping from tree to tree in the blazing Spanish sunlight is so exotically colourful that it is difficult to recall that this is a fairly common European bird. It was wonderful to wake to the richly musical sound of its pure and ringing '*weela-weeoo*', coming from the Eucalyptus trees around the *Palacio*. Its grey-green mate is, however, very difficult to distinguish once she is among foliage; her camouflage is very necessary when she is incubating eggs in her beautifully woven hammock nest, as this is usually suspended near the pendant tip of a branch, where she would otherwise fall victim to every passing predator.

The Coto Doñana offers such a dazzling succession of spectacular birds that after a while one almost loses the capacity for wonderment. I recall one glorious morning when Golden Orioles, Hoopoes, Bee-eaters, Rollers and Woodchat Shrikes were all seen within the space of five minutes, to say nothing of other less exciting species. Shortly afterwards a bird broke cover near us and swerved off among the trees and someone said, 'It's only another Golden Oriole.' 'Only' indeed! Back in the green woods of England such a sight would have caused us all to cry out with admiration and excitement.

A carbonero on the Puntal trail

15

THE PLANT AND INSECT LIFE

THE flora of the Coto Doñana was found to be surprisingly abundant in species, though obviously not so luxuriant as that in the more verdant parts of Andalucía. Some observations on the general vegetation of the region will be found in Chapter 18. It is unfortunately not possible to include in this book a full list of all the plants identified, but a few comments may be made on some of the more interesting species. Readers will, I hope, forgive the use of scientific names where no English vernacular equivalents exist.

The collection of some 240 plants made by the tireless and enthusiastic Lady Huxley, with the assistance of Sir Julian Huxley and Lady Alanbrooke, produced, as we expected, many exciting discoveries. It was afterwards examined by experts at the Royal Botanic Gardens at Kew, whose analysis showed that about eighty per cent of the species have a wide distribution in Europe and North Africa, about forty per cent of them occurring throughout a great part of temperate Europe, and another forty per cent being more distinctly southern, but present in most of the countries bordering the Mediterranean. The remaining twenty per cent consists (*a*) of plants such as *Lobelia urens*, *Carum verticillatum* and *Anagallis crassifolia*, with an 'Atlantic' distribution and more or less limited to the western fringe of Europe and North Africa, though often with a wide latitudinal range; (*b*) of plants, such as *Cistus bourgaeanus*, *Reseda media*, *Armeria baetica*, *Armeria gaditana*, *Pterocephalus lusitanicus*, *Lathyrus nudicaulis*, *Retama sphaerocarpa* and *Leucojum trichophyllum*, either confined to the Iberian peninsula or with a limited distribution in North Africa and the Atlantic Islands. Most of this (*b*) category are distinctly southern plants, limited to the south of Spain, or occasionally extending northwards along the eastern (Mediterranean) coast as far as Barcelona; but *Lathyrus nudicaulis* belongs to the Atlantic element, having its headquarters in north-west Spain and Portugal. It is this fusion of Atlantic, North African and Mediterranean elements that makes the flora of the region so interesting to the botanist. The occurrence of *Hypericum elodes* (Marsh St. John's Wort) was particularly surprising; hitherto this species has been found in Spain and Portugal only in the north and in the Balearic Islands, so that the Coto Doñana station is very isolated.[1] The unexpected presence of this plant, and of *Lathyrus nudicaulis*, which was previously known only in the north of the Iberian peninsula, suggests that careful investigation in the region might reveal further examples of such isolated survival.

In the dry scrub regions the most typical shrub was of course the Cistus-like, yellow-flowering *Halimium halimifolium* (*see* Plate LIV). Several species of true Cistus were found, two of the most beautiful being the white *C. salvifolius* and *C. bourgaeanus*; the Rock Rose *Tuberaria guttata* was another colourful species inhabiting this region.

A patch of the small, daisy-like *Anacyclus clavatus*, which is a widely distributed Mediterranean species, was found one day with what appeared to be brilliant red stamens. The effect was most striking. Closer examination showed that this colour was caused by a heavy infestation of the Red Mite *Balaustinum murorum*, which often occurs in enormous numbers on the southern exposures of houses in some parts of Europe. A rare member of the small family of *Empetraceae* was discovered; this was *Corema album*, which somewhat resembles a large version of our native Crowberry *Empetrum nigrum*; it is very locally distributed in Spain, but is a characteristic flower of the Cádiz region. Dyer's Camomile *Anthemis tinctoria* was common; this plant was formerly cultivated in Britain to provide a yellow dye and used to be mixed with blue Woad *Isatis tinctura* to produce green.

[1] A single record from Algeciras has since been noticed in Font Quer's *Geografia Botanica*.

Six species of the numerous Silene family were identified; these were *S. laeta*, *S. gallica*, *S. hirsuta*, *S. colorata*, *S. nicaeënsis* and *S. stricta*. The luxuriant *Urginea maritima*, which has an enormous bulbous root almost as big as a Rugby football, was evidently much sought after by Wild Boar, to judge from the numerous signs of rooting wherever they grew. This interested us very much in view of the fact that it is from this plant that the rat-poison 'Squill' is manufactured.

Numerous sedges and rushes occurred around the *marismas* and lakes. One of the large sedges was *Cyperus rotundus*, representing a tropical genus. We found our common reed *Phragmites communis* growing to a height exceeding 18 ft. in one locality; also identified were the xerophile rushes *Juncus maritimus* and *J. subulatus*, the bulrush *Scirpus maritimus var. monostachys*, the sedge *Carex otrubae* and the marram grass *Ammophila australis*. Marram Grass was extensively used for thatching by the local peasants; this is no longer permitted in England on account of the importance of the plant in binding the dunes in which it grows. Prevention of this wastage on the Coto, combined with an ambitious planting programme, might well retard, if not arrest, the rapid march of the invading dunes.

The smaller flowering plants were very numerous and included many which are cultivated in English gardens. The following are worthy of mention: the Snowflake *Leucojum trichophyllum*, which surprisingly was growing in sandy localities, Love-in-a-mist *Nigella damascena*, the large-flowered Lavender *Lavandula stoechas* and the Sea Lavender *Limonium ferulaceum*, the tall, creamy Asphodel *Asphodelus ramosus*, the small blue Campanula *Campanula loeflingii*, the very fine large Thrifts *Armeria baetica* and *A. gaditana*, the Lupins *Lupinus hirsutus*, *L. angustifolius* and *L. albus*, the scarlet Buttercup *Adonis annua*, the luxurious red Pimpernel *Anagallis arvensis*, the Mignonette *Resida media*, the lovely indigo Grape Hyacinth *Muscaria comosum*, the rare blue Lobelia *Lobelia urens*, the common yellow Flag Iris *Iris pseudacorus*, the pink Jerusalem Sage *Phlomis purpurea* and the showy yellow Everlasting *Helichrysum serotinum*. The beautiful little cerise Gladiolus *Gladiolus segetum*, which is common in the

Mediterranean region, and the blue Spanish Iris *Iris xiphium hispanica* were found almost invariably growing through Gorse bushes, probably as the only means of survival from the ever-hungry Wild Boar. Only three orchids were collected, these being *Orchis laxiflora*, the handsome *Serapias lingua* and *Serapias cordigera*.

The typical trees of the Coto are the Cork Oak *Quercus suber* and Stone Pine *Pinus pinea*. There are however here and there isolated examples of other species and some plantations of Eucalyptus. One of the most interesting of the introduced species was a fine example of the South American Bella Sombra *Phytolacca dioica*, which stands beside the *Palacio*. In the extreme north-western corner of the Coto there are two small streams which are usually dry in summer. These support a considerable number of broad-leafed trees such as Ash, Willow, Elm and Poplar and a dense undergrowth of thorn bushes and Brambles. This region, embracing the Soto Grande and the Soto Chico, is quite unlike the remainder of the Coto. Among the larger shrubs the most typical are the brilliant green Pistachio *Pistacea lentiscus*, the Junipers *Juniperus oxycedrus* and *J. phoenicea* and the big Tree Heaths *Erica arborea*, *E. scoparie* and *E. umbellata*. *E. scoparia* is wind-pollinated and *E. arborea*, which grows to a height of ten feet, partly so.

The various insects which I collected for the British Museum (Natural History) represented nearly 300 species. There is again unfortunately no room in this book to do more than comment on a few of them.

The butterflies were much less numerous than on the east side of the Guadalquivir. At the time of our visits the most common species were the Clouded Yellow *Colias croceus*, the Bath White *Pontia daplidice* and various *Lycaenidae* (Blues). Among the seven species of the last-mentioned genus, four were familiar to us from the British list—the Common, the Silver-studded, the Holly and the Mazarine Blues. One of the most beautiful butterflies collected was *Euchlöe belemia*, a relative of our Orange Tip, which does not occur in northern Europe. We observed single specimens of the Purple Emperor *Aptura iris*, the Camberwell Beauty *Nymphalis antiopa* and the Scarce Swallowtail *Papilio podalirius*. Painted Ladies,

Brimstones, Red Admirals, Speckled Woods and Green Hairstreaks were fairly numerous. Most of the moths collected were not on the British list, but we identified the Striped Hawk-moth *Celerio livornica*, the Rush Pearl *Nomophila noctuella*, the Powdered Wainscot *Arsilonche albovenosa*, the Delicate *Sideridis vitellina*, the Lackey *Malacosoma neustria*, the Crimson Spotted *Utetheisa pulchella* and various commoner species.

In the Halimium scrub there was a very heavy infestation of the tick *Hyalomma excavatum*. This is a common species throughout southern Europe and North Africa, its hosts being chiefly cattle, camels, buffalo, sheep, goats and swine, though it has been reported as attacking humans in Egypt, Asia Minor, Russia and France. It certainly lost no time in convincing us that Spain should be added to the official list and we were in great trouble with it every time we worked in the scrub areas. Bites from this creature produce symptoms akin to influenza.

The Scorpion *Buthus occitanus* occurs in the sandy regions of the Coto. It is not a very large species, being no more than 3 in. long; its sting is very painful but not dangerous. A very colourful Mantis *Empusa pennata* was found among the yellow Halimium blossoms. The beautifully scalloped abdomen of the nymph (we did not find the winged adult) was mauve with yellow markings, the remainder of the body and long, spidery legs being bright green. The *guardas* called it the 'Santa Teresa', from the prayerful attitude of its heavily armed front pair of legs, with which it seizes its prey.

The grasshoppers and crickets were numerous and colourful. The two specimens illustrated in Plate LV are typical. The big green grass-hopper *Acrida mediterranea* occurred chiefly around the verdant edges of the *marismas*. The Bush Cricket *Decticus albifrons*, which looks like a cream-coloured grasshopper with a long, up-turned neck, was found in the sandy regions, as one would expect from its colour. Both species were so large that they looked like small birds in flight. The most numerous cricket on the Coto was the Mole Cricket *Gryllotalpa gryllotalpa*, which provided a major item in the diet of Hoopoes, Great Grey Shrikes and several other birds. It was also eagerly sought by Wild Boar. The specimens we collected were of this species, but Tono Valverde has also seen *G. africana* on the Coto.

Among the beetles, *Pimelea costata* and the big-jawed *Scarites polyphemus* were found in very large numbers under Cork Oak trees. On the mud-flats Scarab Beetles *Scarabaeus cicatricosus* were common and we collected a number of their interesting dung balls, in which they lay their eggs; we saw several trundling the balls backwards for considerable distances. In the muddy water of the *marismas* the commonest beetle was *Cybister laterali-martinalis*. This resembles the Great Water Beetle and is carnivorous. The numerous dragonflies and damsel-flies were, of course, very much in evidence and many were beautifully coloured. I have mentioned them in Chapter 11. They also are important in the diet of many birds, especially the Bee-eater.

We did not attempt to collect any spiders, but mention must be made of the big Tarantula *Lycosa tarantula* which Abel Chapman illustrated in his books. This grows to about $2\frac{3}{4}$ in. across the legs and is quite a formidable-looking creature, though, of course, much smaller than its tropical relatives. Its bite is said to be exceptionally painful.

I have already referred in a previous chapter to the Ant Lion *Palpares hispanicus*. In its larval form it makes very skilful pits in the sand and lies in wait at the vortex, with its huge pincer jaws ready to seize ants and other insects which fall in; it assists this process by rapidly flicking sand over them, to prevent them from escaping. As a winged adult it resembles a very large, broad-winged dragonfly, with beautifully spotted wings measuring as much as $4\frac{1}{4}$ in. across. Another quite exquisite flying insect which we found was *Nemoptera sinuata*, which has the most attractive 'streamers' behind its spotted wings. The colourful and butterfly-like *Ascalaphus baeticus*, which has brilliant yellow and black patches on its transparent wings, was also a lovely creature; this was found chiefly among the Halimium blossoms. The insect which gave all of us the most trouble was the big grey Horse Fly *Tabanus autumnalis*. This had a very severe bite and the unpleasant skill of alighting on one's neck or arms without being perceived until too late.

16

OUR LADY OF THE DEW

THE annual religious festival of *Nuestra Señora del Rocío* (Our Lady of the Dew) has been celebrated at Pentecost for at least 500 years at the isolated village of El Rocío, some twelve miles to the north of the *Palacio*. It is known that when Christopher Columbus set sail from Sanlúcar on 30 May 1498, on his voyage to South America, he had been delayed in order that the crews of his six ships might first attend the festival. The end of our 1956 expedition happened to coincide with Pentecost, and, as all the *guardas* and the servants at the *Palacio* were going to the ceremony, some of our party decided to accompany them. The films they made of this magnificent spectacle were of outstanding interest.

I cannot do better than quote Abel Chapman's notes concerning the origin of the festival, as they appeared in his *Unexplored Spain*, published in 1910: [1]

Twelve hundred years ago, when Arab conquerors over-ran Spain, much treasure of the churches, with many sacred emblems, relics, etc., were hurriedly concealed in places of safety. But not unnaturally, since Moorish domination extended over 700 years, all trace or record of such hiding-places had long been lost, and it was merely by chance and one by one that, after the Reconquest, the hidden treasures were rediscovered.

The story of the recovery of our Lady of the Dew is related to have occurred in this wise. A shepherd tending his flocks in the neighbourhood of Almonte was induced by the strangely excited barking of his dog to force his way into

[1] *By kind permission of Messrs. Edward Arnold (Publishers) Ltd.*

the dense thickets known as La Rocina de la Madre (a wooded swamp, famous as a breeding place of the smaller herons, egrets and ibises), in the midst of which the dog led him to an ancient hollowed tree. Here, half-hidden in the enormous trunk, the shepherd espied the figure of 'a Virgin of rare beauty and exquisite carving', clothed in a tunic of what had been white linen, but now stained dull green through centuries of exposure to the weather and dew (rocío).

Overjoyed, the shepherd, bearing the Virgin on his shoulders, set out for Almonte, distant three leagues; but being overcome by fatigue and the weight of his burden, he lay down to rest by the way and fell asleep. On awakening he found the Virgin had gone—she had returned to her hollow tree. Having ascertained this, and being now filled with fear, he proceeded alone to Almonte, where he reported his discovery. At once the Alcalde and clergy accompanied him to the spot, and finding the image as related, a vow was then and there solemnized that a shrine, dedicated to *Nuestra Señora del Rocío*, should be erected at the very spot.

Whether this is the correct history or not is uncertain, as there are several versions, each successive chronicler throughout the centuries having doubtless added to or modified the original. One version states that it was a hunter who found the Virgin, another that it was a man in charge of a herd of breeding mares. Yet another claims that the Virgin returned to the tree after having been carried as far as Almonte. Apparently the name of the Virgin was officially changed three times, the earliest inscription on the effigy, in Latin, calling it 'Our Lady of the Cures'; later this was changed to the Spanish inscription '*Nuestra Señora de las Rocinas*', after the locality in which it was found; some time in the seventeenth century it was altered finally to '*Nuestra Señora del Rocío*'. Other familiar names in use today are '*La Blanca Paloma*' (The White Dove) and '*La Reina de las Marismas*' (the Queen of the Marismas), though these are chiefly employed in greeting during Pentecost.

The Virgin was credited with a number of miracles and her fame quickly spread. The inhabitants of Almonte alone escaped the great plague of 1649–50 and the minute spring of water at El Rocío suddenly became capable of slaking the thirst of thousands of men and beasts. The shrine was enlarged and richly endowed with rare jewels and embroidery. An order of neighbouring Brotherhoods was founded, each having a replica of the effigy, and the movement spread rapidly throughout the region. Today it has thirty branches. Every Whitsun a great pilgrimage is made to the original shrine, from all the surrounding countryside and even from as far afield as Sevilla.

To the simple countryfolk the festival is the one great event of the year. The spring and autumn *ferias* in the big towns such as Sevilla and Jerez are certainly bigger and more magnificent, but they lack the superbly uncommercialized setting, the atmosphere and the primitive religious fervour of the Rocío. Here the bare-footed sturgeon fishers of the Guadalquivir and the charcoal burners of the *pinares* mingle with the titled grandees, to pay equal homage, to dance, sing and drink and to forget for a few joyful hours the problems and hardships of the world. Even the late King Alfonso XIII used to take part in the pilgrimage.

For weeks before the great event the women and girls sit in the sunshine at the doorways of their houses, sewing and mending the glorious Andalusian dresses they will wear and talking of the conquests they made on the last occasion or hope to make. The men busy themselves overhauling and decorating the ceremonial harness for the ox-carts. The oxen and horses are groomed until they shine like satin. The high, lumbering carts with 6-ft. wheels, resembling the covered wagons of the American frontiersmen, are freshly painted and decorated with ribbons and garlands of pink, yellow and mauve flowers. Lace curtains and frilled ribbons are fitted beneath the arched white canvas canopies. The wagon carrying the local religious relics is magnificently draped in silver. Each village party travels in a separate procession, at the head of which is carried the effigy of the Virgin and the stiff pennant of the region. The head of the local Brotherhood has the privilege of carrying couched on his stirrup a slender wand, topped by a miniature silver effigy of the Virgin.

The great day dawns and the processions set off across the flowering plain, to the accompaniment of rhythmic clapping, singing, castanets, guitars, pipes, bells, tambourines and drums. Ox-carts, mule-carts and donkey-carts are crammed with women and girls. Young *caballeros* and elderly men alike, clad in the traditional costume of tight, short jacket and flat-brimmed *sombrero*, carry behind them their wives or sweethearts riding *a ancas* (pillion) with their multi-coloured dresses becomingly draped. A few more daring girls ride their own horses astride, but still wearing the modest long dresses and with scarlet or white flowers in their raven hair. The villages gradually empty and remain deserted for several days, or, in the case of the distant localities, even for three weeks.

Among the nobility who made the long journey on horseback was the Duchess of Medina Sidonia, a strikingly beautiful young woman wearing a becoming white riding habit and flat-crowned *sombrero*. Also present was the Princess Esperanza Rocío, wife of the Pretender to the Brazilian throne, tall and fair in gay Andalusian costume. Don Mauricio's father, Don Manuel González Gordon, who never misses the festival, did the cross-country ride from La Plancha, on the bank of the Guadalquivir, to the *Palacio* and on to El Rocío between 7.30 in the morning and dusk. He is still a superb horseman and thinks nothing of spending all day in the saddle. At the age of seventy-one he even took first place in a horse race! Other journeys, made in procession by the Brotherhoods, were more leisurely. The largest caravan, of thirty-six wagons, came from Triana, taking four days to make the trip. The list of towns represented was full of mellifluous, romantic names, such as Sanlúcar de Barrameda, La Palma del Condado, Villamanrique de la Condesa, Carrión de los Céspedes and, of course, Jerez de la Frontera.

Nearing the Mecca the processions begin to converge and the crowds to thicken. Greetings are shouted and the continuous clapping increases in volume. The young men gallop madly up and down the slow-moving lines, rearing their fine arab horses to admiring cries from the girls. The excitement mounts from minute to minute as the white, pink and yellow buildings and the venerable church of the shrine come in sight. The sun blazes down from a cloudless sky and a high golden pall of dust hangs over the scene. The pace slackens to a halting walk and the noise mounts to fever pitch. At each crowded café terrace compliments and badinage are shouted, flowers tossed and toasts drunk. The girls are in seventh heaven under a barrage of admiration.

Finally the church is reached, and there in the fine arching doorway stands the glittering, life-size *Señora del Rocío*. The noise does not abate one fraction, but genuflexions and signs of the cross are made and some of the gorgeously caparisoned oxen and horses are even made to kneel also before passing by. One by one the parties take up their allotted places around the outskirts of the village and picnic meals are produced. Wine and sherry flow like water. As the sun sets there are visits to be made and much neighbourhood gossip to be exchanged and *copitas* to be drunk with old friends. Night falls and still the singing and dancing continue. Bitter rivalries are forgotten under the magic spell of *La Blanca Paloma*. The patient oxen lie sleeping, their crimson finery still about them. The elderly folk snatch a few hours' sleep in the wagons, but to the young not a precious moment is to be wasted. Dawn finds most of them still drinking and dancing.

Whit Sunday dawns. The day is devoted to religious duties, chief of which are the High Mass and the ceremonial *Rosario*, which takes place in the evening. It is the following day which is the climax. The sacred effigy, under its magnificent gold, silver and white canopy, is carried on a heavy platform on the shoulders of forty or more perspiring stalwarts, who are constantly replaced by others eager for the honour. By tradition only those from Almonte, the senior branch of the Brotherhood, may carry the effigy. There is a song from Almonte which refers to this honour:

> *Nadie toque a la Virgen,*
> *Nadie se atreva,*
> *Que son hombres de Almonte*
> *Los que la llevan.*

Roughly translated this means 'Nobody touch the Virgin! Let nobody dare! It is the men of Almonte who carry Her.' Every seven years the effigy is taken to visit Almonte by the inhabitants. The seventeen kilo-

196

LV Some insects and arachnids of the Coto Doñana. 1 Mole Cricket *Gryllotalpa gryllotalpa.* 2 Horse Fly *Tabanus autumnalis.* 3 Hover Fly *Volucella elegans.* 4 Scorpion *Buthus occitanus.* 5 *Nemoptera sinuata.* 6 Mantis (nymph) *Empusa pennata.* 7 *Ascalaphus baeticus.* 8 Ant Lion *Palpares hispanus.* 9 Grasshopper *Acrida mediterranea.* 10 Tarantula *Lycosa tarantula.* 11 Bush Cricket *Decticus albifrons.* 12 Scarab Beetle *Scarabaeus cicatricosus.* 13 *Scarites polyphemus.* 14 *Pimelea costata.* 15 Water Beetle *Cybister laterali-martinalis*

LVI *a.* At the Rocío festival open-air dancing continues day and night, to the accompaniment of flutes, drums, castanets and rhythmic clapping. *b.* This flashlight picture, taken at a lighted oil-lamp in the *Palacio*, indicates the mosquito problem

metres are covered in seventeen hours by the struggling mass of men, who endure with joy the frightful journey under the burning sun, fighting to retain their positions under the huge platform until they drop. On the last occasion they took with them forty casks of wine for refreshment, but, as a sacrifice, consumed only two. Every few hundred yards of the way a young priest shouts a prayer with the full power of his lungs, and this is repeated in a thunderous roar by the physically exhausted but spiritually exalted concourse.

The great procession moves on at snail's pace amidst a densely packed pedestrian multitude, which surges around it like a tidal wave. In the background, pressed stirrup to stirrup, a thousand mounted spectators clap their hands rhythmically. Men and women in the front ranks press forward to touch the shrine, regardless of the fierce efforts of the Almonte men to keep it to themselves. From time to time a cripple, a childless wife or an aged beggar succeeds in climbing on the swaying platform itself to touch the robe of the effigy. Tears of religious ecstasy stream down happy faces and the cries of 'Viva la Virgen!' and 'Viva la Blanca Paloma!' are deafening. Back and forth and from side to side the shrine surges. The noise, heat, dust and kaleidoscopic blaze of colour stun the senses of the onlookers. Looking down on the crowd from a balcony is like looking at the densely banked exhibits of an enormous, animated flower show.

The procession makes the rounds of all the visiting Brotherhoods assembled in the village square, each of which is blessed in turn. As it reaches the centre of each Brotherhood group, the local priest is hoisted on the shoulders of his parishioners and shouts his Salve at the top of his voice. The journey around the Brotherhoods would require less than fifteen minutes at normal walking pace. Today it requires more than four hours. The effigy on its platform might be lifted by a dozen men. Today nearly fifty are tightly jammed beneath it, fighting, sweating and shouting; many are in the last stages of physical exhaustion, but with eyes closed and faces contorted they stagger onwards. Finally Our Lady of the Dew is ceremoniously returned to the altar of the church, where she is placed with her feet resting once more on the ancient hollow tree trunk in which the shepherd found her so many hundreds of years ago. Mass is then celebrated. Even within the sacred precincts the intense emotion of the crowd is unabated, hundreds of men and women still clapping and shouting 'ole, ole, ole!'

During the processions and festivities our cinematographers shot hundreds of feet of film. Everywhere they were met with smiles and greetings. Drinks were pressed into their hands until, as one put it, he was obliged to abandon photography in the interests of Anglo-Spanish friendship. Not so the indefatigable Roger: as soon as dusk fell he produced his stroboscopic flashlamps and succeeded in obtaining a unique series of pictures in colour of the magnificent *fandango* and *sevillana* dancing, until long after midnight.

Strangers from the outside world are rarely privileged to see the Rocío festival. The remoteness of the locality and the difficulty of access fortunately combine to protect it from all modern influence. Long may it survive in all its primitive splendour!

Only the men of Almonte may carry her

LVII The processions of decorated ox-wagons arriving for the annual religious festival of Our Lady of the Dew, which has taken place at the village of El Rocío, on the northern boundary of the Coto Doñana, for the past five hundred years or more

17

FAREWELL, WILDERNESS

O N THE eve of my final departure from the Coto Doñana I went for a stroll along the Martinazo trail as the sun was setting. On the way back I stopped, as I usually did, to sit and smoke my pipe on the gnarled knee of a very ancient Cork Oak, which provided an admirable vantage point overlooking the *marismas*. Behind me the sun had dipped below the jagged frieze of the pines on the horizon, leaving the sky flaming with a crimson afterglow. To my right in the distance I could just see the *Palacio*, its white walls tinted a pastel shade of pink. To the left the sandy trail swept in a wide curve along what, but for the drought, would have been the water's edge. In front of me the boggy ground sloped gently down to a small water meadow, heavily pock-marked with the rootings of Wild Boar and starred with yellow Iris and other bog plants. In the high clumps of Brambles on either side a Nightingale and a Melodious Warbler poured forth a contrapuntal stream of vespers. Above me in the thick foliage a Bonelli's Warbler sang occasional sibilant trills and a Pied Flycatcher made sallies into a haze of midges, snapping its bill loudly on its victims.

On a grassy spit beyond the water meadow a dozen Fallow Deer stood watching me cautiously. Behind them stretched mile upon mile of brown, yellow and green rushes, intersected here and there by ridges of higher ground on which hundreds, if not thousands, of cattle and horses were grazing. Far out, where water still lay in a hidden *caño*, a long line of twinkling white wings proclaimed a tern roost. Finally, forty miles beyond, above the darkening haze, lay the dimly seen peaks of San

Cristobal. It was a scene of indescribable tranquillity, in which I could feel again the strange sensation of timelessness and limitless space which I had known previously only in the great African deserts.

Presently, as my intrusion became forgotten and as I merged motionless into the shadows, watchful eyes began to stray and life picked up its threads around me. A Moorhen crept out of the rushes and began paddling among the irises. A heavy body stirred in the reed-bed and soon I heard the juicy *chomp chomp chomp* of a Wild Boar munching a succulent root. A blue-tailed Sand Lizard scurried across the warm sand near my feet, closely pursued by her red-tailed mate. An emerald-green Tree Frog, no larger than my thumb-nail, climbed slowly up a reed-stem, on the tip of which hung a resplendent yellow and black *Aeshna* dragonfly, its quivering wings softly gleaming. An anxious Jackdaw, which had been circling my tree, decided that danger was past and dropped into its nest-hole, to be greeted by a muffled chorus from its hungry nestlings. A Black-winged Stilt and a Spotted Redshank glided silently down to the water meadow and began feeding, with never a glance my way. The stilt walked slowly, lifting one long red leg delicately after the other, but the redshank hurried hungrily from one likely spot to another, probing urgently into the rich mud. By now the Fallow Deer had ceased waving their long, sensitive ears towards me and had resumed their grazing, only the stag raising its questing nose from time to time to catalogue the passing scents. Its antlers were still in velvet, but it was a lovely animal, its rich, tawny coat handsomely spotted with white.

The singing from the undergrowth gradually ceased and the silence became absolute. Then, close to my ear, I caught an infinitesimal scratching of sound from a long procession of big black Wood Ants, which were industriously carrying caterpillars and other food in single file up the trunk of the Cork Oak, to a nest under the loose bark. A portly Dor-Beetle blundered across their path and was instantly attacked by several ants, which hastily dropped their burdens to deal with the intruder; as the beetle scurried away the ants hurried back into line and continued their tireless labour, with that strange urgency which so deeply fascinated

Henri Fabre. A dainty Clouded Yellow butterfly, disturbed from its resting place on a starry Asphodel, fluttered briefly towards the tree; there was a flash of black and white and a loud snap as the Pied Flycatcher swooped, and one delicate yellow wing spun slowly to the ground, like the falling petal of a wilted flower. From the lush tangle of vegetation by the water meadow a Quail began piping its monotonous 'quic . . . quic-ic'; attracting no response, it stopped equally suddenly. Watching for the bird to emerge, I spotted something clambering laboriously out of a deep crack in the mud. It was a Mud Frog, a handsome little creature called *Pelobates cultripes*, with heavily mottled dark brown and white skin and very protuberant eyes. This is the most numerous frog of the Coto. Tono Valverde once calculated its density on the fringe of the *marismas* during a 'plague' year as about 300 to an area of 10 × 10 yards. It is often the chief prey of water snakes, rats, herons, Black Kites and Barn Owls. As I watched, the frog scrambled quickly across the dangerous open ground and dropped into the safety of another hole.

Overhead, the last flights of egrets and small herons swept past with slowly measured wing-beats, on their way to their roosts in the Algaida thickets. Only the birds at the tail of the procession were hurrying, anxious not to be separated from their companions in the dusk. Far away behind me in the pine woods the first Red-necked Nightjar began to beat out its drum-like song. The life of day was fast giving way to the life of the night. I turned my head to look back at the last traces of the afterglow and saw for a fleeting instant the superb silhouette of a lordly Red Deer stag, standing fifty paces from me, with nose held high to test the dangers of the evening air before venturing down to the water. It saw my movement and bounded, with a crash of branches, back into the undergrowth. The spell was broken. Man, the hateful intruder, was again revealed. A Rabbit thumped its warning and bolted for its burrow. Alarm notes sounded on all sides and heads were everywhere jerked up alertly. The stilt and the redshank rocketed away, yelping. The Jackdaw flew from its hole, calling a harsh 'chack, chack'. The Fallow Deer scampered a few paces, then stood, taut and spring-heeled, their eyes wide and ears cocked.

Sadly I rose and knocked out my pipe. Night was crowding swiftly over the *marismas* and the trees were now etched black against the sky. I walked slowly back down the silent trail. Tomorrow I would return to England by a twentieth-century turbo-prop airplane, to the hurly-burly of overcrowded London, to neon lights, telephones and relentless clocks, to constant noise and the reek of petrol fumes, to newspapers, recurrent crises and talk of the hydrogen bomb. Tomorrow my footprints in the Martinazo trail would begin to silt over. In a few days or weeks no trace of our expedition would be visible. The winter rains would come again to fill the parched *marismas* and the thirsty earth would drink deep, to store the precious moisture far down in the rich alluvial subsoil against the return of the blazing heat of summer. Most of the birds we had been watching would soon depart and the winged multitudes from northern lands would pour into the Coto to replace them for the winter. The rolling dunes would continue to creep stealthily forward from the west, each tiny grain of sand quietly trickling down the steep frontal edge, to mount slowly up the living trunks of the pines until they were suffocated. Yet before each tree died, a frolic wind would seize perhaps one seed from an open cone and whirl it far beyond the menacing sand, to drop it snugly in a Wild Boar's furrow. There it would germinate and presently an infant pine would spring, green and vigorous, to replace its parent and continue the unending cycle of life, death and regeneration. Above it the eagles would go on crying, triumphant in their mastery of the skies and, as time passed, would come to build their eyries in its branches. Beside it the Red-legged Partridges would lead their downy chicks to shelter from the sun and at night the prowling Lynx would scent their tiny footprints and would seek them in the darkness. Out over the scrub, each spring morning would bring forth a million yellow blossoms on the Halimium bushes, to wither in the heat of noon and be replaced by a million more again at dawn. Seasons would come and go, but our beloved wilderness, the Coto Doñana, would dream on through the years, its solitude and beauty remaining, please God, unblemished.

18

PAST, PRESENT AND FUTURE

BY E. M. NICHOLSON

(Ecologist to the 1957 Coto Doñana Expedition)

THE birds and other animals of a region are what they are because of past as well as present conditions of soil, climate and vegetation. In order to understand the bird-life of the Coto Doñana in the past, present and future it is therefore necessary to have some understanding of the region's place in ecological history and geography, and of the forces by which nature has brought about its present shape and character.

Ecology has been defined quite simply as studying the relations of animals and plants to their environment and to one another. The Coto is one of the outstanding ecological demonstration areas in all Europe. To visit it without grasping its basic ecology would be to repeat in essence Charles Darwin's experience at Cwm Idwal, in Snowdonia, when at first he failed to appreciate its geological significance. 'Neither of us,' he afterwards wrote, 'saw a trace of the wonderful glacial phenomena all around us . . . yet these phenomena are so conspicuous that a house burnt down by fire did not tell its story more plainly than did this valley.'

As we ride over the Coto and its neighbouring *marismas* we are continually seeing how nature has moulded them. Before and during the Tertiary epoch, which began some seventy million years ago, the Betic Massif became buckled up between the continental pressure of shifting Africa to the south and the rigid line of what is now the Sierra Morena to the north. This great squeeze thrust up a mountain dome whose remains now dominate both sides of the Strait of Gibraltar, and left a corresponding deep depression submerged beneath the sea following the course of the present Guadalquivir valley down to the Coto.

As it is the fate of mountains over the millennia to be eroded away and carried down in particles to the sea, the Betic Depression over long ages became filled with sediment until eventually, helped by uplifting, it rose above the sea in the form of the delta of the Guadalquivir, opening out just below Sevilla, and advancing to fill the gap between the higher ground behind Huelva and behind Jerez de la Frontera. This delta, it so happened, faced south-west out on to the Atlantic and was thus exposed to much the same south-westerly gales as the British Isles, while the coastal current, running from north-west to south-east towards the Strait, caught it with full force once the Sevilla-Huelva-Jerez triangle was filled up.

The combined effect seems to have been to arrest the further outward growth of the delta along roughly its present line, and to begin throwing back on the beach in the form of sand much of the fine sediment which had formerly been gradually deposited to build the delta farther out to sea. This ample material, now surplus and literally rejected by the Atlantic, was transformed and piled up to build first a long finger of temporary sand bars and eventually a more permanent line of sand dunes, pointing south-east from near Huelva towards Jerez and Cádiz. In course of time this bar of sand strangled the living delta and blocked every exit of the Guadalquivir to the sea except the still surviving extreme south-easterly one near Sanlúcar de Barrameda, about twenty miles north of Cádiz. This entry, now only about half a mile across, cannot be closed, owing to the strong flow of the tidal Guadalquivir, nor can it readily be deflected yet farther south, since it has already been forced against the harder Tertiary rocks around Sanlúcar and Chipiona.

The Coto, therefore, is part of a battlefield of opposing forces of nature. Wind and sea are working together to block the delta of the Guadalquivir, which they have already reduced to a simple river mouth. The sea, however, is now helping to defeat this process, partly by the scour of its strong tides, which help to keep open the remaining mouth,

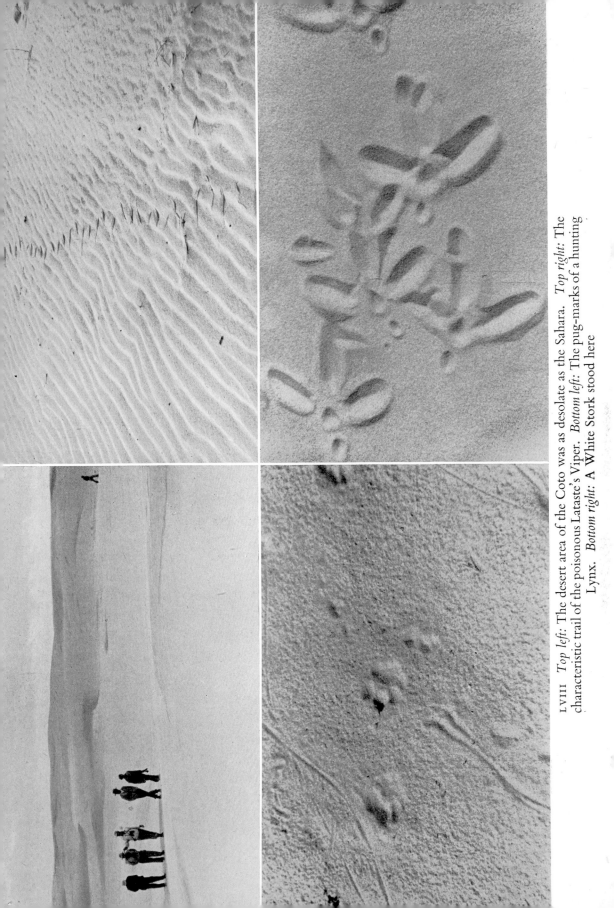

LVIII *Top left:* The desert area of the Coto was as desolate as the Sahara. *Top right:* The characteristic trail of the poisonous Lataste's Viper. *Bottom left:* The pug-marks of a hunting Lynx. *Bottom right:* A White Stork stood here

LIX *Top left:* Typical vegetation at the edge of the dunes. *Top right:* Tony Miller indicates the height of the advancing dunes. *Bottom left:* 30-ft. Stone Pines being buried by sand. *Bottom right:* Phil Hollom in a typical *corral* area of Stone Pines and Halimium scrub

and partly by seasonally flooding the *marismas* with water so salt that it represses rank growth of vegetation which would help to build up the surface even more quickly. The river for its part tends to nullify its own power to keep open its course to the sea, by bringing down so heavy a burden of silt. Some of this, once discharged into the sea, feeds the supply of sand which is constantly tending to enlarge the immense sand-spit barring the delta, while the rest, checked in its down-stream progress by tide or floods, is deposited as silt and helps to raise the *marismas* farther above sea level. A similar process has in the past comparatively few centuries transformed Romney Marsh in Kent from a series of salt lagoons to rich but ornithologically dull pasture land.

The delta constantly demands comparison with that other great bird-haunted delta of south-west Europe, the Camargue, which (if human factors are excluded) is in a more stable phase. The Rhône delta has escaped blocking, partly because of the *Mistral* blowing strongly from the land at right angles to the coast, which with other local winds tends to demolish dune systems as soon as they take shape. The Rhône also flows more strongly than the Guadalquivir and the currents and tides of the Mediterranean are too feeble to matter seriously; the Camargue therefore has not developed the great tracts of dunes and shifting sands which diversify and dominate the Coto, but it has retained larger and more permanent lagoons, both of fresh and saline water, than the *marismas*.

It might be expected that as sedimentation raises the surface of the landlocked Guadalquivir delta lands and the many now obsolete and dying former channels become blocked, the salinity of its soil and waters must fall. This is a point of decisive importance for the bird-life. Certain species, notably the Flamingo and the Avocet, need a diet dependent on extensive standing waters of fairly high salinity in order to survive as breeding birds. Others, notably the Pratincole, probably depend indirectly on salinity to restrict vegetation growth which would otherwise make the ground unsuitable for them. If salinity declines and expanses of saline water shrink or dry up, these species are likely to decline too, the danger signals being diminishing breeding success and increasing frequency of non-breeding behaviour by adults. There is reason to suspect that the Flamingo may be far advanced along this road already, and that on the *marismas* it is in course of becoming a species represented merely by non-breeding stocks still drawn by old custom to an ancestral haunt no longer suitable for reproduction. It may be that the Camargue, which has largely retained its permanent saline lagoons, has recently taken over from the *marismas* the role of the main breeding area for a common south-west European stock of Flamingoes.

Although recently much excellent survey work of the delta has been done by Spanish scientists and engineers, further investigation over a longer period will be needed. The trend towards more or less salinity may well be different in different parts, according to distance from the sea and from the tidal channel of the Guadalquivir. The river itself is extremely saline at all times, except when in flood, from its union with its old course, the Brazo del Este some thirty miles inland, or in dry seasons nearly as far up-stream as Sevilla. The average salt content of the ground-water found in parts of the *marismas* is as high as fifty grammes per litre (as against only thirty-seven in the Mediterranean), but the highest proportions naturally occur on the *marismas* near the river mouth, where salinity is stored in the sub-soil and is replenished by frequent flood tides and seepage, and where the washing effects of fresh water are most rarely experienced.

Plants, with their varying thresholds of salt tolerance, are reliable indicators of salinity when we know enough about their functioning. This unfortunately is not yet the case on the *marismas*, but it seems reasonable to assume that in general *Salicornia* and associated plants mark out the tracts of higher salinity, while the various sedges, rushes and reeds reflect areas of lower salinity. The situation is, however, complicated by the fairly regular flooding from December to April with water no doubt containing varying proportions of salt in different parts of the *marismas*, and by the extremely fine alluvial soil, containing no coarse elements of above two millimetres in diameter and composed as to four-fifths of slime or clay particles actually less than one-twentieth of a millimetre in diameter. Such compact alluvial soil, reaching down to great depths, is almost as impervious as concrete both to water and to aeration; but for this the attraction of reclaiming it for farm crops would be irresistible. However, it is a historical fact that as recently as Roman times the whole of this low-lying area was a vast lagoon called the *lacus lagustinus*, and the *marismas* with their already impressive vegetation must therefore have risen and developed within comparatively few centuries. We know that such processes tend to accelerate naturally in their later phases, and the shape of things to come is perhaps foreshadowed by the fringe of the Coto, from El Rocío southward past the Palacio de Doñana, where broad water-courses prominently marked on the most recent maps can be crossed unobserved, being no longer perceptible on the ground. In such conditions, where freshwater sources are much nearer than the salt river channel, salinity seems bound to decline.

The *marismas* today are low-lying tracts within about 10 ft. of sea level and flooded to a depth of between 1 and 2 ft. for about four or five of the winter and spring months of every normal year, except for scattered small islands, or *vetas*, rising just clear of these inundations. The breeding season of the birds usually coincides with the gradual recession of the flood and for four months or more in summer and autumn a dry period follows. There are no training banks on the main river, or drainage channels into it, to interfere with this natural process, but reclamation and drainage schemes are proceeding within about seven miles. Although dry seasons such as the expedition experienced in 1957 are exceptional, the long-term prospect seems to point towards a more or less rapid reduction in the extent of regular flooding and in the salinity of at least the *marismas* of the Coto Doñana, to the detriment of the birds dependent on such conditions.

Turning now to the drier side of the Coto, it is necessary to discuss more fully the character of the Arenas Gordas—the great sand barrier, nearly forty miles long and from two to nine miles broad, forming the coast between the mouths of the Rio Tinto and the Guadalquivir. In extent and shore-line this dune area is of similar magnitude to all the

dune areas in England put together; being so immense it differs from
them not only in degree but in kind. Its greatest sand ridges, rising to
340 ft. at El Asperillo, just north of the Coto boundary, are probably the
highest in Europe.

The terminal finger, about ten miles long and only between two and
three miles wide, is below the present Coto Doñana and is presumably
the section of most recent origin. It is also the only section in direct contact
with the Rio Guadalquivir, which is at some points locally undermining
and eroding it from the rear. Another characteristic of this section is the
extent and maturity of its woodland cover, consisting almost entirely of
Stone Pines (*Pinus pinea*). These were introduced only within the past
century or two, and have helped to fix the dunes. Their success in this
respect has its limits however, since for miles along the north of this
section immense piles of unstabilized sand are advancing slowly eastwards
on to the *marismas* in successive waves, overwhelming everything in their
path, including even large, mature pine woods growing 20 to 30 ft.
high. The next section northwards, forming the present Coto Doñana,
is more extensive and more varied, broadening out from two or three
miles across at its south-eastern end to more than five miles a little
north of the *Palacio*. It exhibits a complete series of dune evolution, from
bare beaches and embryonic young fore-dunes to both stabilized and
mobile high dune ridges separated by flat, damp depressions, called in
England 'slacks', often colonized by pine woods. Farther inland the sand
relapses into a semi-arid flattened plateau showing some affinities to the
Breckland of East Anglia and, like Breckland, diversified by some refresh-
ing and unexpected sheets of fresh water.

Most of these freshwater lagoons are so aligned as to suggest that they
may have originated in a long-lost mouth or arm of the Guadalquivir,
later cut off from both the sea and the main river. This line of lagoons
separates the higher, largely mobile and raw dunes and pine woods lying
to the west, from the stabilized and flattened-down sandy table-land to
the east and north, between the freshwater lagoons and the saline *marismas*.
That low table-land, at about 45 to 60 ft. above sea level, includes,

especially towards its eastern fringe, some of the richest of the Coto habitats. Here it is pleasantly dotted with fine Cork Oaks, giving it a park-like appearance, and broken in its moister hollows by tall and dense tangles of Tree Heath and of Bramble and Bracken. All these plants need water and they are plain indicators of the underground reservoir beneath the seemingly arid surface of the Coto. The hydrology of this region does not seem to have been worked out, but the most probable explanation is that most of the rainfall quickly soaks through the highly porous sands, to be held up in their lower layers by the impermeable floor of alluvial silt which everywhere underlies it slightly above sea level. Prevented from sinking downwards by the silt, or from leaking out westwards by the counter-pressure of the Atlantic Ocean, this large reservoir of ground-water seasonally floods the low-lying slacks, where part of it is lost by evaporation or absorbed by plants, including the Stone Pines, which nearly all grow on these lower and wetter sites. The residue overflows eastwards to the *marismas* in a series of springs emerging on the slopes, where the sands reach their inland limits and cease to cover the underlying silt. It is at these verdant places that nearly all the few habitations of the region, including the Palacio de Doñana, are naturally sited; the exceptions are in the far north and near one or two of the freshwater lagoons and along the vulnerable and otherwise deserted coast, where guard-posts have been required since the Middle Ages. It is this copious seepage of fresh water over the margin of the *marismas* from the reservoir under the sands which gives this border zone something of the fertile character of an oasis or river-side. Paradoxically the Guadalquivir is so full of salt that its banks are semi-desert, while the edges of the Coto table-land and dunes form as it were the right bank of an imaginary stream rich in nearly all the plants and animals which a great river should have, including, for example, occasional stands of reeds exceeding 18 ft. in height in isolated places.

The examination of the present-day animal and plant ecology of the Coto was greatly aided by the work of members of the 1957 expedition in listing the vertebrates and higher plants and in defining the main animal and plant communities according to habitat types. These are scientifically described and illustrated by Don Antonio Valverde Gomez in his paper 'An Ecological Sketch of the Coto Doñana' (*British Birds*, January 1958). The brief account of the individual habitats which follows is based on the same material, but is necessarily much more condensed and differs somewhat in scope. The two different pictures, however, simply represent the same view looked at from different angles.

For convenience all the habitats are related to a transect line representing the successive stages which an observer would meet along a seven-mile walk north-east from the Atlantic shore near Matalascañas past Santa Olalla and the *Palacio* and out across the Madre and the *vetas* to the *Salicornia* zone on the *marismas* east of the Coto Doñana. For the sake of completeness a few important features which do not fall along this line are introduced at the nearest appropriate point.

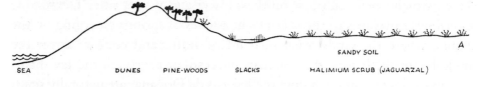

SEA · DUNES · PINE-WOODS · SLACKS · SANDY SOIL · HALIMIUM SCRUB (JAGUARZAL) · A

A (CONT.) · HALIMIUM SCRUB (JAGUARZAL) · CORK OAK SAVANNAH · JUNCIGRAMINETUM · MUDDY SOIL · MARISMAS

Transect of the Coto Doñana, from the sea to the *marismas*

After J. A. Valverde

The Atlantic shore of the Coto is sandy, shelving and nearly straight, unrelieved either by topographical incidents or even by the presence of natural objects larger than pebbles. Rocks are virtually unknown and shore vegetation is sparse. Kentish Plovers and probably Caspian Terns are the only breeding birds. Flocks of Oystercatchers, Sanderlings, Grey Plover and other passing waders rest on the sands. Behind the foreshore the low white fore-dunes carry Marram grass here and there on their low crests, which are constantly being blown inland by on-shore winds. In rear of each line of dunes are the low slacks, where water stands long enough to support clumps of rushes (*Juncus*) and patches of coarse grassy herbage. The bird population is very thin, Thekla Larks and Stone Curlews being almost the only regular breeding species. Here, however, is the spring halting-place of small birds which have just migrated over-sea from Africa; during a migratory 'rush' the few stunted pine shrubs become alive with Melodious, Olivaceous, Rufous and other warblers, and such other visitors as flycatchers and Woodchat Shrikes.

Next come higher ridges of dunes, rising to 50–70 ft. and often so mobile that any pioneer plants and trees colonizing them are liable to find their dunes collapse through undercutting by wind erosion, while those growing in between are smothered by advancing waves of sand varying from 2 to 40 ft. high. This is an almost birdless zone, but many lizards and snakes move, at considerable risk, between the sparse patches of cover, and are hunted particularly by Short-toed Eagles, a few pairs of which breed in the crowns of some of the most advanced Stone Pines. Here also is the haunt of the very rare Carrion Crows of the Coto, which seem to take curiously little interest in the *marismas*.

Immediately in rear of this forbidding country, exposed to wind, intense sun and desiccation, are the more extensive moist slacks dominated by Stone Pines and called locally *corrales*. These *corrales* may extend to hundreds of acres of more or less open pure pine wood, averaging perhaps 25–30 ft. high with scattered clumps of Bramble and patches of rough herbage, and often dominated by threatening walls of mobile sands, which appear in some cases to be burying them at rates possibly exceeding 30 ft. annually on a front hundreds of yards long (*see* Plate LIX*c*). These pine woods are systematically exploited by itinerant charcoal burners, who must by their trimming, cutting and gathering and burning of twigs and litter materially handicap the trees in bringing about soil improvement. These pine woods, except for a few isolated outliers on the plateau to the north-east, extend only in straggling spinneys beyond the line of latitude 37°N, being succeeded by sparse Junipers (*Juniperus oxycedrus* and *J. phoenicidae*), which also occur in places among the pines.

In the pine woods there is a fairly dense population of breeding birds, among which the most characteristic are probably the Hobby, Red-necked Nightjar, Raven, Azure-winged Magpie, Wood Lark and Orphean Warbler and a pair or two of Spanish Imperial Eagles. Others, such as the Black Kite, Great Grey Shrike, Wood Pigeon, Blackbird and Sardinian, Melodious and Dartford Warblers (in the Bramble clumps) occur here and in other habitats. The pine wood being only of modern origin, its birds must be recent colonists, either from outside the region or from other neighbouring habitats, according to their breadth of tolerance. It is a little surprising therefore to find how generally the more closely sociable Azure-winged Magpie has almost annexed this habitat, leaving the also numerous European Magpie to nest chiefly in low bushes outside the woods—a differentiation much sharper than the corresponding division between the Jay and Magpie in north-west Europe.

Between the east of the larger *corrales* rise some of the highest ridges of dunes, not infrequently attaining more than 60 ft. and at some points even rather more than 100 ft., including tawny glaciers of shifting sand whose steep, eastward-facing escarpments are sometimes so loose and precipitous as to be barely negotiable. Just south of our transect line these shifting masses have reached the edge of the *marismas*, on to which fresh water flows from the many springs at their bases. Farther north, however, the sand has become levelled and fixed, sloping down first into low, moribund, crater-shaped lines of dunes enclosing barren plains. Here begin sparse low clumps of the pale grey cistus-like Halimium with its ephemeral yellow morning blossoms, which in increasing density dominate most of the remaining sand plateau.

It is here, still only a mile or two from the Atlantic, that the arid surface is abruptly broken by the attractive freshwater lagoons, mostly of only a few acres, with their lawn-like surrounds of short green grass bordered by rushes and their cool expanses of fresh water, unbroken except by a few isolated clusters of reed-mace and rushes. The breeding water-birds of these lagoons are the Great Crested and Little Grebes, Purple Heron, Mallard, White-headed Duck, Moorhen, Coot and

Crested Coot, possibly also the Red-crested Pochard, Ferruginous Duck and Marbled Teal. In former times, when these lagoons were larger, a number of other interesting species, including the Glossy Ibis, used to breed on them. Flocks of Curlew, Knot and other migrating waders, and of terns, including Black Terns, halt here on passage, and are joined in aerial flycatching by hundreds of visiting Pratincoles from the *marismas*. Parties of Yellow Wagtails use the grass verges.

Passing on eastward, there follows a broad belt of heath country, called in Spanish *jaguarzal*, divisible into a number of well-marked zones. Of these the poorest are the occasional burnt areas or cleared strips, or the sparse Halimium heath, where few birds are found except Red-legged Partridges, Stone Curlews and Thekla Larks. Next comes the Halimium heath mixed with more or less Gorse and Broom, in which the typical birds are Magpies and their vigorous and unfailing parasites the Great Spotted Cuckoos, and also Dartford Warblers and (where scattered low trees or thick shrubs occur) some Great Grey and Woodchat Shrikes. The richer zones consist largely of depressions with a high water-table, representing more advanced counterparts of the slacks among the dunes, and supporting such tall luxuriant shrubs as Pistachio (*Pistacea lentiscus*), Tree Heath and tall Bramble thickets and Brooms. Here the typical birds are the Nightingale, the Sardinian and Melodious Warblers, the Stonechat in small numbers and the Red-necked Nightjar. Sardinian Warblers overlap with Dartfords, but prefer the higher and denser types of cover, while Dartfords favour the lower and more open stands. It is in a more northerly extension of this zone that is located the great Coto heronry, about half a mile or more from the *marismas* (*see* Chapter 7).

Over these eastern heathlands are scattered, with increasing frequency towards their eastern fringe, numbers of Cork Oaks, which form the favourite nesting sites of the Kite, Black Kite, Kestrel, Barn Owl, Little Owl, Green Woodpecker, Jackdaw and Great Tit, and are favourite feeding places for Melodious and other warblers, Spotted and Pied Fly-catchers, Golden Orioles, Woodchat Shrikes and other birds passing in numbers on migration.

Also scattered within this zone are a very few houses and out-buildings, where the Swallow, Spotless Starling and House-Sparrow are the most characteristic birds, with an occasional pair of Hoopoes, while the adjoining small patches of cultivation are the favourite habitat of Goldfinches. By contrast, the other series of structures which are strung out along the coast are occupied by larger birds, such as a pair of Peregrines, Kestrels, Little and Barn Owls and Jackdaws, presumably because their form as watch-towers offers the only suitable breeding sites for such species, while their uncultivated and barren surroundings will not support small passerines.

The *marisma* birds do not come over frequently to the Coto except for some visits by ducks, terns and Pratincoles, principally to the lagoons, and the use of a small area for breeding by herons, which hunt mainly over the *marismas*. But the birds breeding along the Coto fringe feed extensively over the *marismas*, especially the Spotless Starlings, Jackdaws, White Storks and Kites of both species. It is along the *marisma* edges that the concentration of breeding and foraging predators is greatest, no doubt because here are the most frogs, voles and other attractive prey species, especially the Rabbit, which was probably native here long before it was introduced to Britain.

As the surface slopes down for some 20 to 30 ft. to less than 10 ft. above sea level, the sands cease to overlay the silt except in a few small raised fans, where *Anacyclus clavatus*, a flowering plant closely resembling Camomile, dominates the short herbage and Bee-eaters burrow their nests in the flat ground side by side with the surface-nesting Pratincoles and Short-toed Larks. On the steeper slopes the crest of dense Bracken and Brambles overlooks green, rushy, Rabbit-grazed pastures, where Savi's and Fan-tailed Warblers and Yellow Wagtails breed, and non-breeding Black-tailed Godwits, Lapwings and other waders congregate.

Immediately below, less than 5 ft. above sea level, is the richest zone of the *marismas*, formed here by the yard-deep stagnant channel of the Madre de las Marismas, where ribbons of tall reed-mace, reeds and rushes shelter grebes of all three local breeding species, Coots, Moorhens, some Purple Gallinules, Marsh Harriers and Great Reed Warblers, while

Black and Whiskered Terns, Black-winged Stilts and several species of ducks haunt the surrounding marshes.

Beyond is a broad, low zone covered with a sedge called in Spanish *Castañuela*, which is attractive, as long as it is flooded, to Coots and various grebes. In normal years it is on the *vetas*—islands ranging from a few acres down to a fraction of an acre—that most of the many breeding waders nest, especially the Pratincoles, Lapwings, Black-winged Stilts, Avocets, Redshanks and Kentish Plovers. These islands are never flooded, the next highest ground being the very extensive zone covered by Glasswort (*Salicornia*), a shrub which grows in clumps a foot or two high, spaced widely over the baked, cracked mud and supporting (at least in the abnormally dry season of 1957) a remarkably dense breeding population of Short-toed Larks and rather fewer Lesser Short-toed and Calandra Larks and of Yellow Wagtails, with a sprinkling of Stone Curlews, Pin-tailed Sandgrouse and Montagu's Harriers. This zone, which extends far beyond to the bank of the Guadalquivir, completes the transect.

The dry habitats of the sandy Coto and the wet habitats of the silty *marismas* are both rich in wild life, including Red and Fallow Deer, Wild Boars, Lynxes and many other mammals, reptiles, amphibians and invertebrates which there has been no space to discuss in this brief ecological outline. The different habitats, as has been seen, have their characteristic species, yet all are interlocked, and it is the broad series of differing opportunities for existence which make this delta so remarkable for its fauna and flora. But this is not all. Placed on the hinge between Europe and Africa, the region has been able to draw on an exceptionally wide range of species to build up its riches, and has not suffered the disastrous impoverishment of successive Ice Ages, or of geographical and climatic isolation. It has also, to a very rare degree, been shielded by vigilance and care over many generations from the damage inflicted almost universally in Europe by modern economic exploitation. It therefore forms a natural monument of outstanding importance and scientific interest, by the preservation of which from disturbance and development the present owners and Spain itself set an example to the world.

A FINAL WORD
from the Author

The expeditions to the Coto Doñana took place primarily for scientific reasons. It may well be that readers of this book may wish to see for themselves the wonders of the region. In fairness to the owners, I must however make it quite clear that it is a private property. It is the express wish of the owners that it should be preserved as a sanctuary in the strict sense of the word and that it should not suffer the inevitable disturbance which occurs in so many nature reserves to which visitors are given access. It would distress me greatly if the publication of my book should defeat this laudable objective, which is one I am sure readers will heartily endorse. Visitors can nevertheless see the majority of the wild-life represented on the Coto Doñana, with neither difficulty nor risk of disturbance, in the surrounding regions of Andalucía, which are readily accessible. Many of the most interesting species of birds can usually be observed without even leaving the main roads, as anyone who has motored from Sevilla to Gibraltar will know. Certain species which are scarce on the Coto are, indeed, more easily seen to the east of the Guadalquivir.

To those bird-watchers who may decide to visit Andalucía I warmly recommend Ronda, Despeñaperros and Arcos de la Frontera for mountain species; Huelva and the Cádiz settling-beds for waders; the Olive groves and Cork Oak and Stone Pine woods and farms between Sevilla and Jerez de la Frontera for the smaller passerines; the big raptors and vultures may be seen almost anywhere. If bird migration is the chief interest, then Cape Trafalgar and Gibraltar will be outstandingly rewarding. A tour of these localities will also provide opportunities to see some of the most beautiful scenery in the south of Spain.

Appendix 1

THE BIRDS OF THE COTO DOÑANA REGION

Note: This first list represents only those 193 species seen on the Coto Doñana in the course of the three expeditions. A separate list is given of a further 29 species seen on the eastern side of the Guadalquivir and in the adjacent *sierras*. Subspecies have been ignored in these lists. The periods of observation varied from mid-April to early June. Additional species have, of course, been seen by different observers on other occasions, and at different times of year. Spanish names employed are those adopted by the Sociedad Española de Ornitología.

Key: B = breeding; ?B = probably breeding; M = passage migrant; V = vagrant; F = feeding regularly, but not breeding, on the Coto. No attempt is made to indicate the quantitative status of the species.

Species	Spanish Name	Key
Great Crested Grebe *Podiceps cristatus*	Somormujo lavanco	B
Black-necked Grebe *Podiceps nigricollis*	Zampullín cuellinegro	B
Little Grebe *Podiceps ruficollis*	Zampullín chico	B
Gannet *Sula bassana*	Alcatraz común	M
Heron *Ardea cinerea*	Garza real	B
Purple Heron *Ardea purpurea*	Garza imperial	B
Little Egret *Egretta garzetta*	Garceta común	B
Squacco Heron *Ardeola ralloides*	Garcilla cangrejera	B
Cattle Egret *Ardeola ibis*	Garcilla bueyera	B
Night Heron *Nycticorax nycticorax*	Martinete	B
Little Bittern *Ixobrychus minutus*	Avetorillo común	B
Bittern *Botaurus stellaris*	Avetoro común	B
White Stork *Ciconia ciconia*	Cigüeña común	B
Spoonbill *Platalea leucorodia*	Espátula	B
Glossy Ibis *Plegadis falcinellus*	Morito	F
Flamingo *Phoenicopterus ruber*	Flamenco	F
Mallard *Anas platyrhynchos*	Anade real	B
Teal *Anas crecca*	Cerceta común	?B
Marbled Teal *Anas angustirostris*	Cerceta pardilla	B
Garganey *Anas querquedula*	Cerceta carretona	B

217

Species	Spanish Name	Key
Gadwall *Anas strepera*	Anade friso	B
Wigeon *Anas penelope*	Anade silbón	M
Pintail *Anas acuta*	Anade rabudo	B
Shoveler *Spatula clypeata*	Pato cuchara	?B
Red-crested Pochard *Netta rufina*	Pato colorado	B
Tufted Duck *Aythya fuligula*	Porrón moñudo	M
Pochard *Aythya ferina*	Porrón común	?B
Ferruginous Duck *Aythya nyroca*	Porrón pardo	B
Common Scoter *Melanitta nigra*	Negrón común	M
White-headed Duck *Oxyura leucocephala*	Malvasia	B
Grey Lag Goose *Anser anser*	Ansar común	F
Egyptian Vulture *Neophron percnopterus*	Alimoche común	F
Griffon Vulture *Gyps fulvus*	Buitre común	F
Black Vulture *Aegypius monachus*	Buitre negro	F
Golden Eagle *Aquila chrysaëtos*	Aguila real	F
Imperial Eagle *Aquila heliaca*	Aguila imperial	B
Booted Eagle *Hieraëtus pennatus*	Aguila calzada	B
Buzzard *Buteo buteo*	Ratonero común	B
Kite *Milvus milvus*	Milano real	B
Black Kite *Milvus migrans*	Milano negro	B
Honey Buzzard *Pernis apivorus*	Halcón abejero	M
Marsh Harrier *Circus aeruginosus*	Aguilucho lagunero	B
Montagu's Harrier *Circus pygargus*	Aguilucho cenizo	B
Short-toed Eagle *Circaëtus gallicus*	Aguila culebrera	B
Hobby *Falco subbuteo*	Alcotán	B
Peregrine *Falco peregrinus*	Halcón común	B
Lesser Kestrel *Falco naumanni*	Cernícalo primilla	M
Kestrel *Falco tinnunculus*	Cernícalo vulgar	B
Red-legged Partridge *Alectoris rufa*	Perdiz común	B
Quail *Coturnix coturnix*	Codorniz	B
Water Rail *Rallus aquaticus*	Rascón	B
Baillon's Crake *Porzana pusilla*	Polluela chica	B
Purple Gallinule *Porphyrio porphyrio*	Calamón común	B
Moorhen *Gallinula chloropus*	Polla de agua	B
Coot *Fulica atra*	Focha común	B
Crested Coot *Fulica cristata*	Focha cornuda	B
Oystercatcher *Haemantopus ostralegus*	Ostrero	F
Lapwing *Vanellus vanellus*	Avefría	B
Ringed Plover *Charadrius hiaticula*	Chorlitejo grande	M
Little Ringed Plover *Charadrius dubius*	Chorlitejo chico	?B

APPENDICES

Species	Spanish Name	Key
Kentish Plover *Charadrius alexandrinus*	Chorlitejo patinegro	B
Grey Plover *Charadrius squatarola*	Chortito gris	M
Turnstone *Arenaria interpres*	Vuelvepiedras	M
Curlew *Numenius arquata*	Zarapito real	M
Whimbrel *Numenius phaeopus*	Zarapito trinador	M
Black-tailed Godwit *Limosa limosa*	Aguja colinegra	M
Bar-tailed Godwit *Limosa lapponica*	Aguja colipinta	M
Green Sandpiper *Tringa ochropus*	Andarríos grande	M
Wood Sandpiper *Tringa glareola*	Andarríos bastardo	M
Common Sandpiper *Tringa hypoleucos*	Andapríos chico	M
Redshank *Tringa totanus*	Archibebe común	B
Spotted Redshank *Tringa erythropus*	Archibebe oscuro	M
Greenshank *Tringa nebularia*	Archibebe claro	M
Knot *Calidris canutus*	Correlimos gordo	M
Little Stint *Calidris minuta*	Correlimos menudo	M
Temminck's Stint *Calidris temminckii*	Correlimos de Temminck	M
Dunlin *Calidris alpina*	Correlimos común	M
Curlew Sandpiper *Calidris testacea*	Correlimos zarapitín	M
Sanderling *Croccethia alba*	Correlimos tridáctilo	M
Ruff *Philomachus pugnax*	Combatiente	M
Avocet *Recurvirostra avosetta*	Avoceta	B
Black-winged Stilt *Himantopus himantopus*	Cigüeñuela	B
Stone Curlew *Burhinus oedicnemus*	Alcaraván	B
Pratincole *Glareola pratincola*	Canastera	B
Great Black-backed Gull *Larus marinus*	Gavión	F
Lesser Black-backed Gull *Larus fuscus*	Gaviota sombría	F
Herring Gull *Larus argentatus*	Gaviota argéntea	F
Slender-billed Gull *Larus genei*	Gaviota picofina	B
Mediterranean Gull *Larus melanocephalus*	Gaviota cabecinegra	V
Black-headed Gull *Larus ridibundus*	Gaviota reidora	F
Black Tern *Chlidonias niger*	Fumarel común	B
White-winged Black Tern *Chlidonias leucopterus*	Fumarel aliblanco	V
Whiskered Tern *Chlidonias hybrida*	Fumarel cariblanco	B
Gull-billed Tern *Gelochelidon nilotica*	Pagaza piconegra	B
Caspian Tern *Hydroprogne caspia*	Pagaza piquirroja	?B
Common Tern *Sterna hirundo*	Charrán común	M
Roseate Tern *Sterna dougallii*	Charrán rosado	V
Little Tern *Sterna albifrons*	Charrancito	B
Sandwich Tern *Sterna sandvicensis*	Charrán patinegro	M
Black-bellied Sandgrouse *Pterocles orientalis*	Ortega	F

Species	Spanish Name	Key
Pin-tailed Sandgrouse *Pterocles alchata*	Ganga común	B
Stock Dove *Columba oenas*	Paloma zurita	V
Wood Pigeon *Columba palumbus*	Paloma torcaz	B
Turtle Dove *Streptopelia turtur*	Tórtela	B
Cuckoo *Cuculus canorus*	Cuco	?B
Great Spotted Cuckoo *Clamator gladarius*	Crialo	B
Barn Owl *Tyto alba*	Lechuza común	B
Scops Owl *Otus scops*	Autillo	V
Little Owl *Athene noctua*	Mochuelo común	B
Nightjar *Caprimulgus europaeus*	Chotacabras gris	?B
Red-necked Nightjar *Caprimulgus ruficollis*	Chotocabras pardo	B
Swift *Apus apus*	Vencejo común	M
Pallid Swift *Apus pallidus*	Vencejo pálido	M
Bee-eater *Merops apiaster*	Abejaruco común	B
Roller *Coracias garrulus*	Carraca	M
Hoopoe *Upupa epops*	Abubilla	B
Green Woodpecker *Picus viridis*	Pito real	B
Great Spotted Woodpecker *Dendrocopus major*	Pico picapinos	?B
Wryneck *Jynx torquilla*	Torcecuello	M
Calandra Lark *Melanocorypha calandra*	Calandria común	B
Short-toed Lark *Calandrella cinerea*	Terrera común	B
Lesser Short-toed Lark *Calandrella rufescens*	Terrera marismeña	B
Sand Lark *Calandrella raytal*	(Not named)	V
Crested Lark *Galerida cristata*	Cogujada común	?B
Thekla Lark *Galerida theklae*	Cogujada montesina	B
Wood Lark *Lullula arborea*	Totovía	B
Sky Lark *Alauda arvensis*	Alondra común	V
Swallow *Hirundo rustica*	Golondrina común	B
House Martin *Delichon urbica*	Avión común	M
Sand Martin *Riparia riparia*	Avión zapador	M
Golden Oriole *Oriolus oriolus*	Oropéndola	B
Raven *Corvus corax*	Cuervo	B
Carrion Crow *Corvus corone*	Corneja negra	F
Jackdaw *Corvus monedula*	Grajilla	B
Magpie *Pica pica*	Urraca	B
Azure-winged Magpie *Cyanopica cyanus*	Rabilargo	B
Great Tit *Parus major*	Carbonero común	B
Blue Tit *Parus caeruleus*	Herrerillo común	B
Wren *Troglodytes troglodytes*	Chochín	V
Blackbird *Turdus merula*	Mirlo común	B

APPENDICES

Species	Spanish Name	Key
Rock Thrush *Monticola saxatilis*	Roquero rojo	M
Wheatear *Oenanthe oenanthe*	Collalba gris	M
Black-eared Wheatear *Oenanthe hispanica*	Collalba rubia	M
Stonechat *Saxicola torquata*	Tarabilla común	B
Whinchat *Saxicola rubetra*	Tarabilla norteña	M
Redstart *Phoenicurus phoenicurus*	Colirrojo real	M
Black Redstart *Pheonicurus ochrurus*	Colirrojo tizón	M
Nightingale *Luscinia megarhynchos*	Ruiseñor común	B
Cetti's Warbler *Cettia cetti*	Ruiseñor bastardo	B
Savi's Warbler *Locustella luscinioides*	Buscarla unicolor	B
Great Reed Warbler *Acrocephalus arundinaceus*	Carricero tordal	B
Reed Warbler *Acrocephalus scirpaceus*	Carricero común	B
Marsh Warbler *Acrocephalus palustris*	Carricero poliglota	M
Melodious Warbler *Hippolais polyglotta*	Zacero común	B
Olivaceous Warbler *Hippolais pallida*	Zarcero pálido	?B
Blackcap *Sylvia atricapilla*	Curruca capirotada	?B
Orphean Warbler *Sylvia hortensis*	Curruca mirlono	B
Garden Warbler *Sylvia borin*	Curruca mosquitera	M
Whitethroat *Sylvia communis*	Curruca zarcera	B
Lesser Whitethroat *Sylvia curruca*	Curruca zarcerilla	M
Sardinian Warbler *Sylvia melanocephala*	Curruca cabecinegra	B
Subalpine Warbler *Sylvia cantillans*	Curruca carrasqueña	?B
Spectacled Warbler *Sylvia conspicillata*	Curruca tomillera	B
Dartford Warbler *Sylvia undata*	Curruca rabilarga	B
Rufous Warbler *Agrobates galactotes*	Alzocola	?B
Fan-tailed Warbler *Cisticola juncidis*	Buitrón	B
Willow Warbler *Phylloscopus trochilus*	Mosquitero musical	M
Chiffchaff *Phylloscopus collybita*	Mosquitero común	M
Wood Warbler *Phylloscopus sibilatrix*	Mosquitero silbador	M
Bonelli's Warbler *Phylloscopus bonelli*	Mosquitero papialbo	?B
Spotted Flycatcher *Muscicapa striata*	Papamoscas gris	M
Pied Flycatcher *Muscicapa hypoleuca*	Papamoscas cerrojillo	M
Collared Flycatcher *Muscicapa albicollis*	Papamoscas collarino	V
Meadow Pipit *Anthus pratensis*	Bisbita común	V
Tawny Pipit *Anthus campestris*	Bisbita campestre	M
Tree Pipit *Anthus trivialis*	Bisbita arbórea	M
White Wagtail *Motacilla alba*	Lavandera blanca	M
Yellow Wagtail *Motacilla flava*	Lavendera boyera	B
Great Grey Shrike *Lanius excubitor*	Alcaudón real	B
Woodchat Shrike *Lanius senator*	Alcaudón común	B

Species	Spanish Name	Key
Masked Shrike *Lanius nubicus*	Alcaudón núbico	V
Spotless Starling *Sturnus unicolor*	Estornino negro	B
Greenfinch *Chloris chloris*	Verderón común	V
Goldfinch *Carduelis carduelis*	Jilguero	B
Siskin *Carduelis spinus*	Lúgano	V
Serin *Serinus canarius*	Serín	B
Chaffinch *Fringilla coelebs*	Pinzón vulgar	V
Yellowhammer *Emberiza citrinella*	Escribano cerillo	V
Corn Bunting *Emberiza calandra*	Triguero	B
Ortolan Bunting *Emberiza hortulana*	Escribano hortelano	M
Reed Bunting *Emberiza schoeniclus*	Escribano palustre	?B
House Sparrow *Passer domesticus*	Gorrión común	B
Tree Sparrow *Passer montanus*	Gorrión molinero	V

ADDITIONAL SPECIES SEEN ELSEWHERE IN ANDALUCÍA

Most of these observations were made within fifty miles of the Coto Doñana; all were made within the periods of the three expeditions. No indications are given as to breeding status, etc., as the areas were not studied in detail. Some species which were uncommon on the Coto were plentiful elsewhere in Andalucía and vice versa.

Species	Spanish Name
Bearded Vulture *Gypaëtus barbatus*	Quebrantahuesos
Bonelli's Eagle *Hieraëtus fasciatus*	Aguila perdicera
Rough-legged Buzzard *Buteo lagopus*	Ratonero calzado
Barbary Partridge *Alectoris barbara* (Gibraltar)	Perdiz moruna
Great Bustard *Otis tarda*	Avutarda
Little Bustard *Otis tetrax*	Sisón
Snipe *Capella gallinago*	Agachadiza común
Rock Dove *Columba livia*	Paloma bravía
Tawny Owl *Strix aluco*	Cárabo común
Alpine Swift *Apus melba*	Vencejo real
Kingfisher *Alcedo atthis*	Martín pescador
Red-rumped Swallow *Hirundo daurica*	Golondrina dáurica
Crag Martin *Ptyonoprogne rupestris*	Avión roquero
Jay *Garrulus glandarius*	Arrendajo común
Chough *Coracia pyrrhocorax*	Chova piquirroja
Alpine Chough *Coracia graculus*	Chova piquigualda
Crested Tit *Parus cristatus*	Herrerillo capuchino

APPENDICES

Species	Spanish Name
Long-tailed Tit *Aegithalos caudatus*	Mito
Short-toed Tree Creeper *Certhia brachydactyla*	Agateador común
Mistle Thrush *Turdus viscivorus*	Zorzal charlo
Blue Rock Thrush *Monticola solitarius*	Roquero solitario
Black Wheatear *Oenanthe leucura*	Collalba negra
Robin *Erithacus rubecula*	Petirrojo
Moustached Warbler *Lusciniola melanopogon*	Carricerín real
Firecrest *Regulus ignicapillus*	Reyezuelo listado
Linnet *Carduelis cannabina*	Pardillo común
Cirl Bunting *Emberiza cirlus*	Escribano soteño
Rock Bunting *Emberiza cia*	Escribano montesino
Spanish Sparrow *Passer hispaniolensis*	Gorrión moruno

Appendix 2

THE MAMMALS OF ANDALUCÍA

(Those recorded on the Coto Doñana are marked*)

*Hedgehog	*Erinaceus europaeus hispanicus* Barrett-Hamilton.
*White-toothed Shrew	*Crocidura russula* Hermann.
*Savi's Pygmy Shrew	*Suncus etruscus* Savi.
Mediterranean Water Shrew	*Neomys anomalus* Cabrera.
Mediterranean Mole	*Talpa caeca occidentalis* Cabrera.
Greater Horseshoe Bat	*Rhinolophus ferrum-equinum obscurus* Cabrera.
Lesser Horseshoe Bat	*Rhinolophus hipposideros minimus* Heuglin.
Mehely's Horseshoe Bat	*Rhinolophus Mehelyi* Matschie.
*Mouse-eared Bat	*Myotis myotis* (Borkhausen).
Natterer's Bat	*Myotis Nattereri* (Kuhl).
Daubenton's Bat	*Myotis Daubentonii* (Kuhl).
*Common Pipistrelle Bat	*Pipistrellus pipistrellus* (Schreber).
Kuhl's Pipistrelle Bat	*Pipistrellus Kuhlii* (Kuhl).
Noctule Bat	*Nyctalus noctula* (Schreber).
*Serotine Bat	*Eptesicus serotinus* (Schreber).
Barbastelle Bat	*Barbastella barbastellus* (Schreber).
Long-eared Bat	*Plecotus auritus* (L.).
*Schreibers' Bat	*Miniopterus Schreibersi* (Kuhl).
European Free-tailed Bat	*Tadarida teniotis* (Rafinesque).
*Badger	*Meles meles marianensis* (Graells).
Beech Marten	*Martes foina mediterranea* (Barrett-Hamilton).
*Polecat	*Mustela putorius aureolus* Barrett-Hamilton.
Weasel	*Mustela nivalis iberica* (Barrett-Hamilton).
*Otter	*Lutra lutra* (L.).
*Wolf	*Canis lupus signatus* Cabrera.
*Fox	*Vulpes vulpes silacea* Miller.
*Genet	*Genetta genetta* (Linné).

*Mongoose	*Herpestis ichneumon Widdringtonii* (Gray).
*Wild Cat	*Felis sylvestris tartessia* (Miller).
*Lynx	*Felis pardina* Temminck.
Rock Ape	*Macaca sylvana* (L). (Gibraltar only.)
Squirrel	*Sciurus vulgaris infuscatus* (Cabrera).
*Garden Dormouse	*Eliomys quercinus lusitanicus* Reuvens.
*Mediterranean Rat	*Rattus rattus frugivorus* (Rafinesque).
*Brown Rat	*Rattus norvegicus* (Erxleben).
*House Mouse	*Mus musculus brevirostris* (Waterhouse).
* „ „	*Mus musculus spretus* Lataste.
*Long-tailed Field Mouse	*Apodemus sylvaticus dichrurus* (Rafinesque).
*Mediterranean Pine Vole	*Pitymys duodecimcostatus ibericus* (Gerbe).
„ „ „	*Pitymys duodecimcostatus centralis* Miller.
„ „ „	*Pitymys duodecimcostatus regulus* Miller.
*Water Vole	*Arvicola terrestris sapidus* Miller.
*Hare	*Lepus europaeus granatensis* Rosenhauer.
*Rabbit	*Oryctolagus cuniculus Ruxleyi* Haeckel.
Spanish Ibex	*Capra pyrenaica hispánica* (Schimper).
Roe Deer	*Capreolus capreolus* Linné.
*Fallow Deer	*Dama dama* (L).
*Red Deer	*Cervus elaphus hispánicus* Hilzheimer.
*Wild Boar	*Sus scrofa castilianus* Thomas.

Appendix 3

THE AMPHIBIANS AND REPTILES OF ANDALUCÍA

(Those recorded on the Coto Doñana are marked★)

★Pleurodele Newt	*Pleurodeles waltl* Michahelles.
Boscá's Newt	*Triturus boscai* (Lataste).
Marbled Newt	*Triturus marmoratus pygmaeus* (Wolterstorff).
★Spotted Salamander	*Salamandra salamandra hispanica* (Wolterstorff).
Painted Frog	*Discoglossus pictus* Otth.
Spotted Mud Frog	*Pelodytes punctatus* (Daudin).
★Southern Mud Frog	*Pelobates cultripes* (Cuv.).
★Canary Islands Hyla	*Hyla arborea meriodionalis* Boettger.
★Marsh Frog	*Rana ridibunda perezi* Seoane.
Midwife Toad	*Alytes obstetricans boscai* Lataste.
Common Toad	*Bufo bufo spinosus* Daudin.
★Natterjack Toad	*Bufo calamita* Laurenti.
★Spanish Terrapin	*Clemmys leprosa* (Schweigger).
★European Pond Tortoise	*Emys orbicularis* (L).
★Greek Tortoise	*Testudo graeca* (L).
★Moorish Gecko	*Tarentola mauritanica* (Linné).
Turkish Gecko	*Hemidactylus turcicus* (Linné).
★Mediterranean Chameleon	*Chamaeleon chamaeleon* (Linné).
★Grey Burrowing-Lizard	*Blanus cinereus* (Varidelli).
★Wall Lizard	*Lacerta bocagei liolepis* Boulenger.
★Ocellated Lizard	*Lacerta lepida* Daudin.
Spanish Sand Lizard	*Psammodromus hispanicus* Fitz.
★Algerian Sand Lizard	*Psammodromus algirus* (Linné).
★Spine-foot Lizard	*Acanthodactylus erythrurus* (Schinz).
★Sand Skink	*Chalcides bedriagai* (Boscá).
Cuvier's Three-toed Sand Skink	*Chalcides striatus* (Cuvier).

Horseshoe Whip-Snake	*Coluber hippocrepis* Linné.
*Ladder Snake	*Elaphe scalaris* (Schinz).
*Southern Bordeaux Snake	*Coronella girondica* (Daudin).
Hooded Snake	*Macroprotodon cucullatus* (Geoffroy).
*Montpellier Snake	*Malpolon monspessulana* (Herm.).
*Lataste's Viper	*Vipera latasti* Boscá.
*Water Snake	*Natrix maura* (L).
Grass Snake	*Natrix natrix astreptophera* (Seoane).

Bibliography

ALLEN, R. P. (1956). The Flamingos: Their Life History and Survival. *Nat. Aud. Soc. Res. Rep.* 5. New York.

ALMAZÁN, DUKE OF (1934). Historia de la Monteria en España. Madrid.

BACA, D. J. (1887). Aves de España. *Mem. Acad. Cienc.* Madrid. 11: 471.

BERNIS, F. (1954). Prontuario de la Avifauna Española. Madrid.

BERNIS, F., and VALVERDE, J. A. (1954). La Gran Colonia de Garzas del Coto Doñana. *Munibe* 1: 1–39.

BERNIS, F., and VALVERDE, J. A. (1954). Sur le Flamant Rose dans la Péninsule Ibérique. *Alauda* 22: 32–39.

B.O.U. List Sub-Committee (1952). Check-list of the Birds of Great Britain and Ireland. London.

BROWN, L. H. (1955). A Flamingo Mystery Solved. *Country Life*, 1955: 164-167.

CABRERA, A. (1914). Mamiferos. *Mus. Nac. Cienc. Nat.* Madrid.

CHAPMAN, A., and BUCK, W. J. (1893). Wild Spain. London.

CHAPMAN, A., and BUCK, W. J. (1910). Unexplored Spain. London.

CONGREVE, W. M. (1947). Spanish Birds in the British List. *Ibis* 89: 276-278.

FONT QUER, P. (1953). Geografia Botanica de la Península Ibérica. *Géographie Universelle* 10: 143-271.

FRUGIS, S. (1954). Osservazioni ornitologiche in Ispagna. *Riv. Ital. Ornith.* 24: 24-35.

GALLET, E. L. (1950). The Flamingoes of the Camargue. Oxford.

HAINARD, R. (1948). Mammifères sauvages d'Europe. Neuchatel.

INGRAM, C. (1956). Shooting the Great Bustard in Spain. *Country Life*, 1956: 1314-1317.

IRBY, L. H. L. (1875). The Ornithology of the Straits of Gibraltar. London.

JOURDAIN, F. C. R. (1936-7). The Birds of Southern Spain. *Ibis* (13), 6: 725-763; (14), 1: 110-152.

LLETGET, A. F. (1954). Sinopsis de las Aves de España y Portugal. *Trab. Inst. Scienc. Nat.* Madrid.

LÜDI, W. (1956). Die Pflanzenwelt Spaniens. *Veröffentl. Geobot. Inst. Rübel in Zurich*, 31 Heft: 1-298. Bern.

LYNES, H. (1912). Field notes on a collection of birds from the Mediterranean. *Ibis* (9), 6: 121-187.

LYNES, H. (1913). Bird notes in two Andalusian Sierras. *Ibis* (9), 6: 454-489.

MERTENS, R., and MULLER, L. (1940). Die Amphibien und Reptilien Europas. *Abh. Senck. natf. Ges.* 451: 1-56.

MOREAU, R. E. (1956). The Iberian Peninsula and Migration. *Bird Study*, 3: 1-25.

MOREAU, R. E. and W. M. (1956). Acerca de la migración otoñal en el Estrecho de Gibraltar. *Ardeola* 3 (1): 59-69.

MOUNTFORT, G. (1954). The Larks of Andalucía. *Ibis* 96: 111–115.

MOUNTFORT, G. (1956). Rare Birds in Coto Doñana. *The Sphere*, 1956: 59–62.

MOUNTFORT, G. (1956). Kite's Castle. *The Sphere*, 1956: 139–141.

MOUNTFORT, G. (1956). The Herons of Coto Doñana. *The Sphere*, 1956: 357–360.

MOUNTFORT, G. (1957). First Pictures of the Spanish Imperial Eagle. *The Sphere*, 1957: 163–165.

MOUNTFORT, G. (1957). The Short-toed Eagle at Home. *The Sphere*, 1957: 233–235.

MOUNTFORT, G. (1958). Migración visible en las Costas de Málaga. *Ardeola* 4 (1).

NICHOLSON, E. M., FERGUSON-LEES, I. J., and HOLLOM, P. A. D. (1957). The Camargue and the Coto Doñana. *British Birds*, 50: 497–519.

PETERSON, R., MOUNTFORT, G., and HOLLOM, P. A. D. (1954). A Field Guide to the Birds of Britain and Europe. London.

PETERSON, R. T., and FISHER, J. (1955). Wild America. Boston.

RIKLI, M. A. (1942–48). Das Pflanzenkleid der Mittelmeerländer. Bern.

SÁEZ-ROYUELA, R. (1954). Liste des Passériformes d'Espagne. *Oiseau*, 23: 93–108; 24: 106–122.

SAUNDERS, H. (1871). List of the birds of Southern Spain. *Ibis* (3), 1: 54–68, 205–225, 384–402.

SAUNDERS, H. (1873). On the ornithology of Spain. *Trans. Norfolk and Norwich Soc.* 73: 16–24.

SAUNDERS, H. (1877). Catalogue des Oiseaux du Midi d'Espagne. *Bull. Soc. Zool. Fr.* 1: 315–327; 2: 11–22, 89–98, 185–208.

SAUNDERS, H. (1884). Notes on the birds of the Pyrenees. *Ibis* (5), 2: 365–392.

SAUNDERS, H. (1897). Further notes on the birds of the Pyrenees. *Ibis* (7), 3: 64–89.

STENHOUSE, J. H. (1921). Bird notes from southern Spain. *Ibis* (11), 3: 573–594.

VALVERDE, J. A. (1957). Notes écologiques sur le Lynx d'Espagne. *La Terre et la Vie*. 1957, 1: 51–67. Paris.

VALVERDE, J. A. (1958). An Ecological Sketch of the Coto Doñana. *British Birds*, 51: 1–23.

VALVERDE, J. A., and WEICKERT, P. (1956). Sobre la migración de varias garzas españolas. *Pub. Grup. Cienc. Nat. Aranz.* San Sebastian.

VERNER, W. (1909). My Life among the Wild Birds in Spain. London.

WITHERBY, H. F. (1922). An ornithological trip to central Spain. *Bull. B.O.C.* 43: 73–74.

WITHERBY, H. F. (1922). Results of a collecting trip in the Cantabrian Mountains, northern Spain. *Ibis* (11), 4: 323–345.

WITHERBY, H. F. (1928). On the birds of central Spain. *Ibis* (12), 4: 385–436, 587–663.

WITHERBY, H. F. (1929). The birds of Spain. *Ibis* (12), 5: 185–186.

WITHERBY, H. F. (1930). On an ornithological expedition in eastern Spain in May and June 1929. *Bull. B.O.C.* 50: 74–79.

WITHERBY, H. F., *et al.* (1938–41). The Handbook of British Birds. London.

YEATES, G. K. (1946). Bird Life in Two Deltas. London.

Index

231

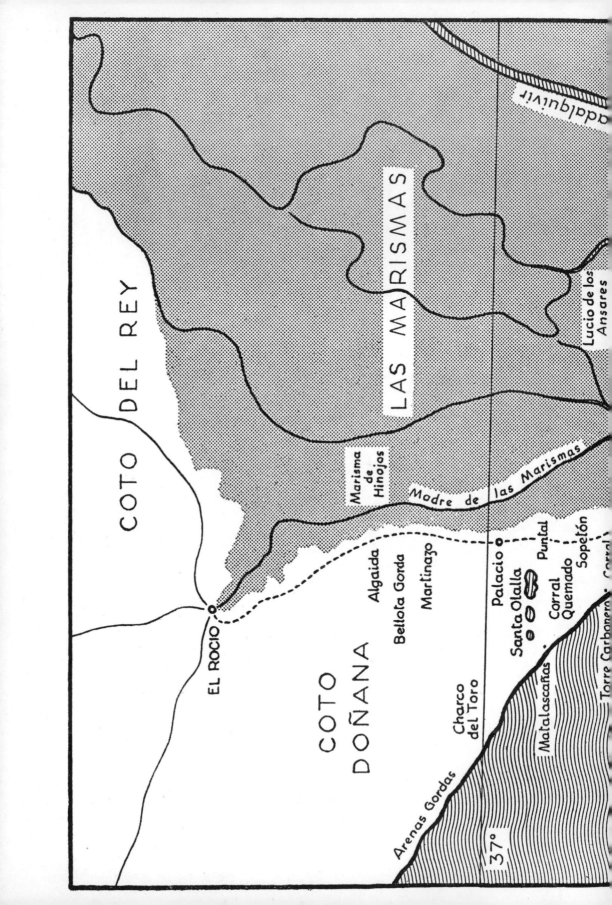